MW00577562

A Determined Spirit

One Woman's Victory
in Catastrophic Illness

A Determined Spirit

One Woman's Victory
in Catastrophic Illness

by
Sharon Craft Moore

Treasure House

An Imprint of
Destiny Image Publishers, Inc.®
P.O. Box 310
Shippensburg, PA 17257-0310

ISBN 1-56043-261-6

For Worldwide Distribution
Printed in the U.S.A.

Treasure House books are available through these fine distributors outside the United States:

Christian Growth, Inc.
Jalan Kilang-Timor, Singapore 0315

Rhema Ministries Trading
Randburg, South Africa

Salvation Book Centre
Petaling, Jaya, Malaysia

Successful Christian Living
Capetown, Rep. of South Africa

Vine Christian Centre
Mid Glamorgan, Wales, United Kingdom

Vision Resources
Ponsonby, Auckland, New Zealand

WA Buchanan Company
Geebung, Queensland, Australia

Word Alive
Niverville, Manitoba, Canada

Inside the U.S., call toll free to order:
1-800-722-6774

Dedication

This book is dedicated to the memory of my father, Silas Edwin Craft, Sr., who the Lord called home to rest on January 12, 1995; to my husband John, my daughters Stacey Renée and Ashley Revée, my goddaughter Deidre, and my godsons Ken, Elijah, Ira, and Cedric.

Acknowledgments

I am thankful to the following people for helping me make this book what it is:

My husband John, for his undying love, encouragement, and assistance;

My daughters Stacey and Ashley for asking permission to disturb me;

My sister-in-law Peggy Howard for her time given in editing my first draft;

My Mom and Dad, sisters, and brothers for encouraging me during my MS struggles;

My church family and saints of God who have prayed for me;

The Multiple Sclerosis Society for books loaned from their library;

Family members and special friends whose support made publication possible;

Dee Dee Chambliss, photo artist.

Contents

Introduction

If I were in control of my life, I think that I would have worked things out differently. There would be no hurt, no pain, no disappointments—of these things my life would be scot-free. But that just goes to show, how little I know about leading, about controlling my life. For you see, all these things have worked together just to make the best of me. God controls my life and my times are in His hands. And I'm learning each and every day to trust Him, come what may. For you see if I were in control of my life, I know that I would have worked things out differently. But my times, all of the good and all of the bad, my times, all of the hurt and all of the pain, my times are in His hands.[1]

The words of this song are a great beginning for this story. I thank God for inspiring the songwriter and allowing me the opportunity to hear it, because the words express exactly how I feel.

What is perceived by the casual observer is only a small part of the overall difficulty I experience each day. It is a proven fact that more often than not we draw our conclusions from what we see—outward appearances. It may not be the correct conclusion, but in our minds it's real all the same. I say this because people have often said to me, "You don't look like anything's the matter. Every time I see you, you look great." I realized how blessed I am that God has sustained me through many trials and that my physical facade hasn't given in to them. One can have multiple sclerosis and not look like he or she has the disease.

Sympathy is not what I have needed or desired; just encouragement, compassion, an attitude of willing service, and genuine concern. Since being diagnosed with multiple sclerosis, I have sometimes experienced insensitivity, and many times I have been inclined to wonder where some people's thoughts are. Do they really understand what it means to be wearing the shoes of a person who has MS, someone who must use a cane, a walker, or a wheelchair to aid their mobility? Then "a determined spirit" says to me, "Sharon, they can't understand because it's not *their* experience." However, each of us must be a good runner in the race of life. We must never forget that the shoe could always be on the other foot. Therefore we must not take walking, feeling, seeing, touching, and other "routine" activities for granted.

For the last two years, I've prayed that God would prepare me for the task of recording my MS experience. He's never failed me. God is faithful. I've wanted to write *A Determined Spirit* for so long. I have always felt that it would be an encouragement and a blessing to someone, whether or not they have MS or some other debilitating disease. I also felt it could serve as a primer for those who don't know anything about MS.

What a comfort it is to know that we don't have to go through anything alone, for God is always there. It is such a relief to know that through the death of Jesus Christ on the cross, the way was paved for "a determined spirit" to receive all the resources required for enduring personal affliction. Jesus is a burden bearer and a sharer of heavy loads. Thank God that we don't have to fight any battle alone, for as First Samuel 17:47 says, "the battle is the Lord's."

One must trust in Jesus Christ as his or her personal Savior in order to have a relationship with Him. Trust in Him today, so He can be *your* burden bearer. I know and trust God for myself, and this story tells how I came to a fuller relationship with Him. He hears every time I pray and cry to Him. I know He sees all that I go through and gives me strength daily.

Whoever is reading this story and going through something, rejoice anyhow! Jesus suffered, so what makes us think that we don't have to go through trials and tribulations? Ecclesiastes 9:11 tells us, "...the race is not to the swift, nor the battle to the strong...." Therefore, I let "a determined spirit" keep me focused on Jesus. In my own strength, I am neither swift nor strong, but the Spirit that lives inside me keeps me pressing on. You can press on too. Be encouraged!

Sharon Craft Moore
January 13, 1994

Chapter 1

Beginnings

Before I formed you in the womb I knew you; before you were born I sanctified you.

Jeremiah 1:5

Childhood

I was born September 19, 1954, at 8:52 p.m. to Silas and Dorothye Craft, in Sandy Spring, Maryland. On the way to the hospital, Montgomery General, Mom passed a church named Sharon Baptist, which inspired her to give me that name. I weighed in at 8 lbs. 2 ozs., and I was healthy. God had already blessed my parents with three girls and two boys. I would now occupy the last position.

For the first 12 years of my life, I lived in a community called Guilford. The section of the road where our house was located is no longer there. It has become part of Interstate 95, in an area that is now Columbia, Maryland. The community was rural, and I didn't have a lot of playmates. My dad had chickens, which supplied us with eggs. We also got various fruits and vegetables from our trees and gardens. I can remember picking strawberries and other crops. There was even a time in my childhood when Dad raised pigs. Back then, that was exciting stuff!

I anxiously awaited going to school so I could meet other peers, something beyond my two imaginary friends, Dorca and Berna, whom I had created. We spent many happy hours together, but by third grade they faded completely out of the picture. I wanted to go to school when I was five years old, but our school had no kindergarten so I had to wait until I was six. Then off to first grade I went. A self-motivated child, I was friendly, loved people, and was a good student. We started class each day with the Lord's Prayer and the Pledge of Allegiance to the American flag. I used to be teased that my voice could be heard all the way down the hall because of its distinctive sound. I had excellent teachers who really valued education and the nuclear family. In fact, they were more than just teachers; they knew your parents and genuinely cared about you. I'm so glad they took the time to invest in me.

In elementary school, I was a Brownie and then a Girl Scout. I loved earning badges. I learned to play the clarinet, and I could also play the piano a little "by ear." My mother was a pianist who often played for soloists and church choirs. I loved to go to her rehearsals, and became upset when I couldn't go along. Sometimes she even let me sing!

When I was in the third grade, I was involved in a car accident while riding to the bus stop with my brother Silas Jr. to pick up my Dad. Our vehicle skidded off the wet road and hit a fire hydrant. I hit the dashboard and injured my forehead and right knee. They took me to the hospital, and I received six stitches in my forehead and seven in my knee. During the summer of that year, 1962, I had plastic surgery performed on both scarred areas. What an experience for an eight year old.

Church revivals weren't new to me. Although church was already an "every Sunday" occurrence, I loved going to revivals. I got to attend most fall revivals where my mother was the pianist for a choir. One particular church always had a female evangelist who preached the Word so eloquently. I loved her! Each time she preached, it was as though she was talking just to me. She would have the hymn "Have Thine Own Way" played at every altar call. Oh how I would cry whenever that music filled the church. That's what I knew I wanted God to do with me—have His way.

When I was in the fourth grade, my church, First Baptist Church of Guilford, had a revival. On the last night, a Friday, I remember the preacher extended the invitation to salvation. He said, "Give me your hand and give God your heart." I knew I wanted God to have my heart. I knew that He loved me and I felt special. At that time I went forward and accepted Him as my Lord and Savior, knowing from that moment on, the Holy Spirit would live inside of me. I became a candidate for baptism and was baptized at a church in Baltimore, Maryland. I was in the family of God, Hallelujah!

In the fifth grade, I had the same teacher who had taught my fourth grade class. She was like an adopted mom for me and some others in the class. We were her "pets." She really watched out for us like we were her own flesh and blood children. While in her class, I remember becoming a majorette. One of our big events was marching down Pennsylvania Avenue near the White House for the Safety Patrol Parade held in May. Since I was the smallest and shortest, I got to lead our group. What an honor!

Racial integration came into the picture when I reached sixth grade. For the first time I was taught by a white teacher. White people were only new to me as public school classmates. I already knew them as neighbors and playmates. I had also fellowshipped with white children at a church we attended during the summer for Vacation Bible School. From sixth grade on, I was educated in an "integrated" environment.

My childhood summers were spent in Bluefield, West Virginia with my maternal grandparents. From ages 7 through 11, my sister Kaye and I faithfully visited our grandparents. Very active in their church, my grandfather was a Deacon and my grandmother was a Deaconess. Nannye, which was what we called my grandmother, was a very special, very proud, and spiritual woman. She wasn't prideful in a negative way, but proud in that she knew who she was in Christ and who she was as a Black woman. Nannye made sure I was in Sunday school and church service every Sunday. I even sang with the children's choir during my summer stays. I had a lot of playmates on my grandmother's street. Even on the next street, I had a friend who taught me hand game routines and let me ride her scooter. Big fun!

One of our regular adventures in Bluefield included going to a funeral parlor, owned by the father of one of my friends, to view the bodies and see the beautifully arranged flowers. We also enjoyed climbing to the top of the ladder attached to a building housing a holiness church. We would look through the window to see church members praise the Lord by dancing, playing tambourines, shouting, and singing. At the time I didn't understand all this release of energy and emotion, but I do now!

Discipline did not escape us in West Virginia. Spankings were rare, but they were swiftly and effectively administered when I disobeyed. One day my sister Kaye and I went to visit at the home of one of our friends and didn't tell Mom. When we returned to Nannye's house, Mom was livid: first, because we didn't have permission to go and, second, because she didn't know where we were. After she corrected us with her rod, the switch, I knew we would never repeat that behavior again. Today I understand and can praise the Lord for the rod of correction.

Leaving my grandparents at the end of the summer was both a happy and sad time. Although I was about to return home to familiar surroundings, I loved the beauty of West Virginia. I knew I would miss the mountains and the naturally air-conditioned mountain air. I wouldn't be able to go to the corner store anymore to buy popsicles, bubble gum, and candy at a moment's urge. Besides, I had to leave my summer friends. It was tough leaving Nannye and Gramps' house and the piano that I enjoyed playing. Nannye always used to have me sing a song called, "Something Within."[1] She would have me sing one verse and the chorus. That song impacted my heart forever and I'll never forget the words:

> I met God one morn', my soul feeling bad,
> Heart heavy laden with a bowed down head.
> He lifted my burden and made me so glad,
> All that I know there is something within.

Chorus:
Something within me that holdeth the reins.
Something within me that vanishes pain.
Something within me I cannot explain.
All that I know is there is something within.

What powerful words!

Junior High and High School

I realized life was changing. I was growing up, and I was on my way to junior high school. Seventh grade was spent in Kansas City, Missouri, where my dad, a Bluefield State College and University of Pennsylvania trained educator, was involved in a community schools program for a trial year. At the end of that year, he would decide whether he wanted to stay or move back to Maryland. We bought a house in an all white neighborhood, not knowing that Black people had never lived in that subdivision before. Some of the neighbors grew to love us and we them. However, all was not peaceful. One family on our street lined up their children in front of our house and had them call us "niggers"—a blatant demonstration of ignorance and racism. We held fast and refused to be run out of the neighborhood, but it obviously wasn't the most pleasant of situations.

To top it off, I went to a large school where I was the only Black girl, and there was only one Black boy. I was culture-shocked! It was a large school district, yet we were the only Black students in the school.

Fortunately, the principal and counselor were as concerned about incidents happening as I was. In fact the counselor told me to come and tell him if anything negative occurred. I only remember one incident that caused physical pain. I was walking down the hall to lunch, and a girl walking behind me took her protractor and stuck me on my rear end. It was painful! I turned around to see the culprit, went to the girl's bathroom to check the injury, then proceeded to the counselor's office to inform him of the incident. He took me to the lunchroom to point out the girl. I obliged, and he took her to the office and dealt with the matter. The counselor was quite upset and apologized for the incident, but no type of apology ever came from the girl's mouth to me. I was truly glad when that trial year was over for Dad. When he asked if we wanted to return to Maryland, there was no hesitation whatsoever! Even though I had a Black friend named Judy, who lived in the city, I was in total agreement about relocating back to Maryland.

In the eighth grade, we lived in Silver Spring, Maryland. I attended a school where Dad was one of the assistant principals. I was on my best behavior because my dad did not play around! Now that I was 13 years old, I started babysitting for our neighbors when a need arose. I would play with or watch toddlers and infants with no problem. Not to boast, but I was a good, trustworthy babysitter and enjoyed it very much. I participated in Girl Scouts for the next two years and even tried some sales by becoming a sales associate for a company that sold cards and stationary items. Christmas cards were a hot selling item. So between being a sales associate and babysitting, I earned extra money.

In the ninth grade I finally got to go to the school zoned for my neighborhood. I was going to school with my friends. Yeah! My extracurricular activities that year included playing in the band and participating in intramural sports.

High school was preparation for college, so there was much more homework. I was a B-average student. I remember one day I was going to leave school with some friends after checking into homeroom. Well, by the time homeroom was over, the principal knew about it and contacted my dad who was still working in the school system. He asked to speak to me, and he told me that I had better not leave school, I had better go to all my classes, and that he would deal with me when he got home. I worried the rest of the day about what my Dad was going to say to me when he got home. He could have earned the "lecturer of the year award." Had there been one I surely would have nominated him. Well, I survived the lecture that evening, but it was rough. He let me know that I better not *ever* try that again, and I never did.

I played intramural basketball, and I was a pom-pom girl. I played in the school band, sang in the school choir, and auditioned for and made the Montgomery County choir. This choir did several recitals for county residents. I really enjoyed that experience.

I had a boyfriend in high school. His nickname was "Demon" and mine was "Devil." Although the nickname "Devil" was born during my high school years, it was only when I got to college that "Devil" was in, and "Sharon" went into hibernation. "Demon" was a nice guy, but I knew when I went to college I would gladly say goodbye to him. I did, however, give him the "honor" of taking me to the senior prom. I had asked my dad beforehand, if I could go to a breakfast and pool party at a classmate's house afterward. He told me to be home at midnight. I felt that curfew was unfair, so I came home at 1:00 a.m. Of course he was waiting up for me. I was called everything except a "child of God." Nonetheless, I survived the lecture once again and awaited my escape to college. I graduated from high school in June 1972.

College Years

In the fall I enrolled at Morgan State University in Baltimore, Maryland. I was excited to be able to leave home and have some freedom. I could now go out without permission from my parents. Yeah!

When I arrived on campus for freshmen orientation in late August, I couldn't meet people fast enough. There were so many. One thing that got its beginning during orientation week was the masking of my name. Almost everyone went by nicknames, so when I was asked about mine, I said "Devil." From that day forward, that's what I was called. No longer Sharon, but Devil—which meant: darn evil, very intelligent, and loud. I thought it was cute at the time, but as I reflect back, especially since having reestablished my fellowship with God, there was *nothing* cute about it. Satan was happy about it I'm sure, because I was giving him honor. I must admit that I took an "out of fellowship with God" break when I was in college, something that I'm not proud of because God hates sin. But, I am so glad that God had His hand on me and has forgiven me for that behavior during that time in my life. I love the Lord so much that I hesitate to even remember that time in my life; however, God was maturing and pruning me even then.

As a freshman, I participated in the marching band as a clarinet player, but I really desired to be a pom-pom girl after having been one in high school. I loved to dance and socialize, so I partied a lot. I made a lot of friends, and we did a lot of things. My grades as a freshman were not averaging "B" overall; they were more like "C+." I knew that I had to focus my mind back on the academics and put my best efforts forward.

During my sophomore year, I pledged Delta Sigma Theta Sorority. What an experience! There were lots of late nights and long days, including much community service and volunteer work and many social events. One valuable attribute I gained from that experience was *learning to share*. I learned how to really share the last of whatever I had; how to make a little go a long way; and how to give of myself to others through volunteer service and projects. It was rewarding! I succeeded in focusing my mind back on academics, and I had a "B" average at the end of the semester. Even though I pledged a sorority, it helped my studying because we went to the library every night during the "on line" weeks. The pledge time was six weeks. We had our initiation ceremony and crossed the "burning sands." I no longer was a "pyramid", a pledgee, but I was now a member of Delta Sigma Theta Sorority, Inc. Yeah!

I was excited about my junior year, for I was moving from a dorm on campus to an apartment. Sharon, the psychology major, would room with Janet, a communications major, and Lucy, an accounting major. We got along well.

During my junior year, I ran for "Miss Junior." Everyone knew me as "Devil," so I had to put "Devil" under my correct name on the ballot. I won and was Miss Junior for Homecoming. Other activities during this year involved my sorority projects and occasional tutoring. I also had to plan what my Senior Seminar Project would focus on and what my plans would be upon graduation.

Senior year I just wanted to complete my Senior Seminar project in psychology and graduate with honors. My mind was set, not on graduate school, but on securing a job and making money. I wanted to work and receive a paycheck. I desired my own apartment, car, clothes, etc. I did not want to move back home, for I had become used to doing my own thing. I was independent. I went where I wanted to go, and when I wanted to go. I knew that I would have to move back home for awhile and readjust to the house rules of my parents. Even though I went clubbing and partying a lot, I knew that would calm down somewhat for I had no car, and I had to respect Mom and Dad. I was moving back home and it was their house. Was I ready for that? Emphatically no! However, I knew that if I wanted to work in the field of psychology, I would need a master's degree at the minimum. That was not my goal. I wanted to change my field of study to business.

I graduated from Morgan State University in May 1976, summa cum laude, with a B.S. in psychology, at the age of 21. I did return home, but I believed that I wouldn't be living there long.

Chapter 2

Independence

...They shall mount up with wings like eagles, they shall run and not be weary....

Isaiah 40:31

Interviewing

Upon moving back home, I immediately combed the employment sections of newspapers. Before I graduated from Morgan, I had interviewed with several companies. Most of them wanted me to relocate out of state, and I had no desire to do so. Therefore that shortened my possibilities. On the home front, I decided to work as a temporary through agencies until I found permanent employment. I wanted to save some money so I could purchase a car and move.

I began the job interview process, interview, after interview, after interview. I really had no experience except typing, filing, and proofreading. Yet one thing was always true throughout my working years, I never worried about a job because Dad had made sure I learned how to type in eighth grade summer school. Boy, am I glad he did! Typing was a valuable skill. I was able to work for temporary agencies until I got a permanent job placement. I'm a great typist, even today (provided I'm not struggling with spasticity in my fingers, or optic neuritis in my eyes).

While in college, I worked each summer with C&P Telephone Company. I just assumed that I would apply for a permanent job with them upon graduation and that I would be hired. I applied, but holding fast to that dream, it was five years before I began working with C&P.

I'll never forget going to take the Civil Service Exam at the Office of Personnel Management in Washington, D.C. I was due there at 8:30 a.m. I caught the bus and got off at the wrong bus stop. It was approximately 8:05 a.m. I had to run seven blocks to get to the Office of Personnel Management. I got there at 8:28 a.m., out of breath and sweating. I successfully completed the exam. And in July 1976, I landed a job with the U.S. Government as a clerk-typist with the Commodity Futures Trading Commission in Washington, D.C.

My First Objective Achieved

I worked faithfully and did overtime as much as I could. I was determined to save a down payment for a car. I knew I would have to achieve the finances for this objective on my own. Dad felt like he had made his contribution by sending me to college. I was an adult now and had to carry my own weight. By November, I was able to buy my first car. A friend of mine had had much to say about Hondas, so I purchased a white Honda Civic. The main thing was that it was in my budget. Perhaps I should have been more patient and waited a little longer. But I was in a hurry. I needed a car! I demonstrated impulsive behavior—and paid for it—ending up with a car that was a "lemon." That car gave me much grief and was in the shop all the time. I tried to take it for its routine maintenance checks on schedule, and every time I did, it came back with a problem it didn't have when I took it. I really believe my car was sabotaged by the mechanics because it was new and I was a female who knew nothing about how to change a flat tire, let alone the idle, oil, etc. I gained valuable maturity lessons from that experience. Thank the Lord. Of course, in the midst of car headaches, Dad and I weren't in agreement about my social life. I knew it wouldn't be long before I left home for good. During these trials, John came into the picture.

Dating John

When I was in high school, at night when I said my prayers, I would say, "Lord, send me somebody." That was a very popular song at that time, and I took it to heart. God answered my prayer with John. We met when he was in law school at Columbia University in New York. My sister Kaye, who was in graduate school at Columbia, introduced us. John was so intellectual and smart. I just knew he wasn't my type. Here he was about to graduate from law school and I was just graduating from an undergraduate school. He was quiet, and I was loud. However, since God was in control of my destiny, all things did work together for good. John, who was from Jackson, Mississippi, decided to accept an attorney position with the Honor Law Graduate Program of the U.S. Department of Justice and move to Washington, D.C.

During one of our regular sister-to-sister telephone conversations, Kaye volunteered, "Sharon, John's in D.C.

now; you better give him a call!" I frowned up my face, but I did give him a call. We made a date for my birthday, but I went out with someone else. I really didn't mean to hurt his feelings, but I did. John had even brought me flowers! I was rather insensitive during that period, but as God would have it, we did begin to date.

I was a smoker when John and I started dating, and he let me know that he did not care for smoking. He preferred a non-smoking "significant other." That was all I needed to hear and quit smoking shortly thereafter. I thank God every time I see someone light up that He delivered me from what could have developed into a deadly habit.

John also told me that he was a "one woman" man. Well, in the time that I graduated and started dating John seriously, I broke up with my friend in Baltimore and stopped seeing a friend I had in Washington. My focus was on John. He was so kind, giving, encouraging, understanding, comical, and fun to be with. He helped me weather storms between my dad and myself, for we weren't seeing eye to eye on a lot of things at that time in my life. I felt I had been to college, I was 22 and not a baby anymore, legal, and could be my own timekeeper and decision maker. Well, Dad didn't see things that way. He told me that I would either live by his rules or I could leave his house. I realized that it was his house, he was my father, and I was to still honor him. So, I chose to prepare to launch out on my own.

During the five years that I dated John, we shared a number of recreational activities, including tennis, swimming, jogging, bicycling, and walk-a-thons. I even took a beginner's roller skating class because we liked to skate on the weekends. I also cannot forget bowling—we participated in league bowling until we got married. Starting in September 1976, I took a ballet class for a year; from September 1977 to June 1979, I took a tap dance class; and September 1979 to June 1981, I took jazz dance. John and I also traveled to the Bahamas, Barbados, Acapulco, and various states within the continental United States. I loved to dance so we did the club and party scene too, although John was not especially keen on either. I was a member of Spa Lady and worked out at least twice a week during the evening. I even taught an exercise class at the church I was attending at the time.

Leaving the Nest

When I moved out it was really time to leave the nest. The tension had just become too thick! My sister Virginia was my saving grace. I moved in with her until I could get an apartment. That was one of the hardest days of my life—leaving home for good, just to return to visit. My mom and I were so close, and when I said, "Good-bye, Mom," I felt like my heart was being ripped out of my chest. I was crying and so was she, but we got through the farewells.

New Jobs, Higher Salary

The job with Commodity Futures Trading Commission didn't last long for me, just five months. It didn't pay enough so I moved on to Montgomery County Government. There I was trained as a Word Processor. I then secured a higher paying position as a Word Processor for a law firm in Washington, D.C. Next, I moved to an engineering firm in Silver Spring, Maryland, as an office manager, again with an increase in pay. After that I moved back to Washington, D.C. to work for another engineering firm as a payroll accountant. This was my last place of employment until I started full time with C&P Telephone Company after my wedding.

I also worked part time at various jobs. One of them was selling art. I've never been thrilled about "sales," especially since I am not a real aggressive salesperson. Nevertheless, I put forth my best effort and it resulted in some healthy monthly sales awards. I continued in sales until I got married. It kept me busy and nurtured my developing desire to start my own business.

More Schooling

During the job transitions, I started attending evening classes at Montgomery College, Ben Franklin University, American University, and Southeastern University. I took accounting and business courses from the fall of 1976 to June 1981. I enrolled in the MBA program at American University, but did not continue after the first year. I decided that I wanted an MS in accounting, so I later enrolled in the master's program at Southeastern University. I withdrew from that program as well before getting married. Grades weren't the problem, I did well. The problem was my mind-set.

Apartment Life

I finally got my first independent apartment in December 1976. It was an efficiency, but it was nice and it was my home. I was working a full and part-time job. I also made my first furniture purchases at this time because my college apartment had been furnished. My purchases consisted of a sleepsofa, a coffee table, a table with two chairs, a television, and a floor lamp. I had a stereo from college that worked just fine. Things were moving right along until I managed to get the chicken pox. I couldn't believe it. Here I was, 22 years old, and I had the chicken pox. But it was real! I believe I contracted it from someone while working in the "boys" department at the Hecht Company. Dad came over every evening to make sure I was all right. (The relationship between my dad and me had not been destroyed. Prayer and time allow hurts to heal and anger to become resolved through forgiveness.)

While living in that first apartment, I met a wonderful person named Beverly. A medical student, she was my next door neighbor and we got along well. We decided to become roommates and move into a two-bedroom apartment in a "luxury" building. That apartment was roach heaven. We later found out that we were over the boiler room, so roaches had a field day in our apartment. Those roaches worked my nerves! We finally broke the lease and moved out. So much for my second apartment. Beverly and I are still friends today, and I'm proud to say she is a practicing dermatologist.

My third apartment was a one-bedroom apartment. This was to be my last apartment before I said, "I do." It was the best one yet, and I loved it. It was a nice, spacious place. I also had furniture from my other two apartments, so I didn't need to purchase any. Thank God!

Insights

From 1976 until my wedding day, I lived the active life of a healthy, worry-free single. The Lord certainly took care of me during that period. Only He could have protected me from some of the things I did and the places I went. But that's God's grace, His unmerited favor, giving me what I didn't deserve. I am so thankful for the love that He demonstrated toward me.

I have many fond memories of my pre-marriage days. I was a happy person, for the only responsibilities I had were for myself—or so I thought. Before being diagnosed with multiple sclerosis, mine was a varied, vibrant, and full lifestyle. However, everything must change. With independence came responsibilities. And, life was about to teach me that God had a purpose for my life, and soon enough I would begin to know what it was.

Chapter 3

What's With the Numbness?

Trust in the Lord with all your heart, and lean not on your own understanding.

Proverbs 3:5

John and I dated for five years. I became tired of just being his girlfriend. I wanted to be his wife. He finally asked me to marry him. I accepted, and we proceeded to make plans and set a date. This process began in August 1980. I then became inundated with all the hoopla that accompanies such a celebration. I worked a lot of overtime, still did recreational things, and was very tired.

Why is my right index finger so numb? I pinched, shook, and smacked it, to no avail. It remained numb. It was Monday, March 30, 1981, and I was employed with the engineering firm in Washington, D.C., in their accounting department. Since I was in the planning mode for our wedding, I just thought my nerves were going berserk. When I mentioned the numbness to my friends in the office, Carmen and Patsy, and some of my family members, they all said the same thing. "You just have a pinched nerve, why don't you go to your doctor?" I really did not want to go to the doctor. That would take time and I had tons of things to do for the wedding. Nonetheless, I called my general practitioner and made an appointment.

I prayed, "Lord, let it not be anything much; I'm getting married soon!" Yes, I knew that God was my heavenly Father and that I was His child, but I wasn't in fellowship with Him like I should have been. I wanted this situation to change in the near future, and I believed that it would. The purpose God had for me was unfolding, so I prayed and sought understanding. I asked God, "What road lies ahead of me?"

By the time my appointment came, on April 7, 1981, the numbness had spread up my arm and down the right side of my body. I was beginning to get very nervous about these changes in my body. When I visited Dr. Robert Wilkinson, my general practitioner, a lot of fact gathering was done. He asked me questions and had me relay to him what had been occurring. Only the numbness and tingling were evident at that point, no other symptoms. My reflexes, coordination, gait, and vision were normal. When a pinprick test revealed my sensitivity was duller on my right side than my left, I was referred to Dr. Richard Edelson at the Neurology Center for further evaluation. (He became the neurologist with whom I would have a long relationship.) I was to visit the Neurology Center in either Bethesda, Maryland, or in Washington, D.C. I came to know the place well! I was thinking to myself, *I hope to find out what this problem is before I say, "I do."*

My first appointment with Dr. Edelson was April 17, 1981. He did a fact gathering interview in which I explained the symptoms that had prompted my concern. During the neurological examination, he looked for "signs," abnormalities detected during the examination. I've learned that "[I]n essence, symptoms are subjective complaints, whereas signs are objective observations."[1]

The neurological exam consisted of looking at my pupils with a ophthalmoscope, which allowed the doctor to examine the visible portion of my optic nerve where it penetrates the eyeball. I was also subjected to pinpricks, raising and lowering of my arms and legs, taps with a rubber mallet on my arms and knees to check reflexes, observation of my balance and gait, and other exercises. At the conclusion of this appointment, I was scheduled for three diagnostic tests: a visual evoked response test, a somatosensory evoked response test, and a CAT scan.

In the visual evoked response test, visual stimuli are placed before the eyes and responses to the stimuli are recorded. This test is considered "by far the most valuable; this is because it can demonstrate unsuspected lesions of the optic nerves in 75% of patients with MS who have never been aware of any previous alteration of vision."[2] In the somatosensory evoked response test, nerves in the arms and legs are stimulated and electrical impulses are recorded from the appropriate parts of the brain. In the CAT scan, a computer assisted examination of the brain is conducted to determine whether any physical evidence of the illness exists on the brain.

I next met with the neurologist on April 24, 1981. John went with me. I was given the results of the visual evoked response test and the CAT scan. Although they were both normal, my numbness still persisted. Tests results in hand, I began to focus my attention on June 6, my wedding. I did not see Dr. Edelson again until May 1982.

Chapter 4

New Husband, New Job

Oh, give thanks to the Lord, for He is good! For His mercy endures forever.

Psalm 136:1

Changes were entering my life. Two were big ones right from the start: a new husband and a new job. I was a productive 27 year old about to embark on the responsibilities of a new family and a new career. On June 6, 1981, I would be married. Five days later, I would begin my new career in management. I would assume two new roles: one, becoming a wife and, the other, becoming a first-level supervisor. I was looking forward to both with great joy. I realized that I would be learning many things in both areas and making many adjustments, but I was focused and ready.

Friday, June 4, came and it was countdown time until the wedding. I was becoming real nervous. My wedding participants arrived from Georgia, New Jersey, New York, Washington, D.C., and Maryland. The wedding party consisted of a matron of honor, a maid of honor, five bridesmaids, a best man, six groomsmen, a ring bearer, and a flower girl. That evening we had the rehearsal and the dinner. I stayed at Mom's house because we had already moved my things into what would be my new home with John. I was so excited! Mom and I had a chance to talk and she said, "Well, Sharon, this is it. You're an adult now, about to be married. I only wish you God's best and much happiness. I'm so proud of you!" Those words were the icing on the cake. I love my mom so much. What an example she is!

I was up early the next morning making sure all the bridesmaids were there and accounted for. I've always considered myself an organized and efficient person. This day was to be no different. Finally, the bridesmaids were prepared, and I was ready to be photographed by the photographer. We anxiously awaited the arrival of the limousine. True to form, the driver got lost, which delayed our planned arrival time at the church. I got there just as the Rev. Dr. Benjamin Hooks, the officiating minister, was coming up the sidewalk. Dr. Hooks, a family friend who at that time was the executive director of the NAACP, had come straight from the airport after arriving on a flight from New York. What timing! I have always been a stickler regarding time. The ceremony began only ten minutes late. At 1:10 p.m., I was married at my home church, First Baptist Church of Guilford in Columbia, Maryland. Sharon Dorothye Craft became the wife of John R. Moore, Esq. In less than an hour, we were no longer singles, but united together as one, Mr. and Mrs. John R. Moore.

After the reception, we were both exhausted so we left for our honeymoon in the Poconos the next morning. We arrived at the resort at lunchtime. We got settled, rested, and prepared for dinner. What fellowship! Being in the same resort with lots of newlyweds created an excitement that was contagious.

Back in our hotel we swam a lot, because we had a suite with a private swimming pool. We met another couple who switched rooms with us one night, so that they could use our pool and we could experience their heartshaped bathtub and bed. I liked our room the best, even with the round bed! We went horseback riding and roller skating. We also played archery, miniature golf, pool, tennis, and participated in other activities. Honeymoons are for sharing intimately and having a wonderful time, and we did just that!

We returned to the Washington area on Saturday. After a brief stop at a church bazaar, we arrived at our first home, a residence John had purchased before the wedding. He had previously lived in a condominium, which was great preparation for securing a house. What a blessing! We unloaded the baggage, settled in, and settled down. Sunday we went over to Mom's and picked up our wedding gifts. We returned home and I prepared myself for work the next day. I would be starting my new job at C&P as a business office supervisor on Monday, July 11, 1981.

I knew that I would be going to Dallas, Texas, for a two-week training period in a couple of months. I was anticipating how I would be accepted because I knew that I would be the youngest supervisor there and had been hired from outside of the company. I knew there would be those who felt that they should have gotten my job because of seniority. Nevertheless, I prayed and asked God to please be with me. He was right there.

Our home had a staircase to the upstairs and steps leading to the basement. I was to learn later what a blessing it is to be able to climb stairs without holding on and to be able to run up and down steps fast and think nothing of it. Our first mistake was not to have a burglar alarm installed immediately after moving in. Soon after we had moved in, I came home from work one day and saw that the curtain at the door was hanging down. From afar, I noticed that a window pane was broken lower on the door. The hole in the pane was round like a softball, as though someone had thrown a ball through it. I started backing up and went to my neighbor's house and called John. He came right home and called the police. Yes, we had been burglarized! With John traveling a lot, I was very uncomfortable about sleeping or staying there alone. We soon secured an alarm system.

In August, I went to Dallas, Texas, for two weeks of training. I missed my husband and just wanted to be at home, but the experience and training were great. The numbness I had experienced before the wedding was gone. I thought it had left my body permanently. I was later to learn what a "remission" and an "exacerbation" meant.

I returned home, and John and I became acclimated as husband and wife once again. One of the goals we had was to find a church home. We both loved the Lord, liked going to church, and were saved. What a blessing that was because the Bible tells us not to be "unequally yoked with an unbeliever." Both of us were on the same sheet of music, and God was *first* in our life. Come what may, we could and would handle it together.

Chapter 5

Diagnosis and Acceptance of Multiple Sclerosis

*...Count it all joy when you fall into various trials,
knowing that the testing of your faith produces patience.*
James 1:2-3

More Tests to Undergo

I returned to Dr. Edelson's office on May 27, 1982.
Two weeks prior to this appointment, I had a new onset of
numbness in my right upper arm and shoulder. It took
tracking and observing my symptoms for approximately
one year before my doctor told me that he was operating
under the tentative diagnosis of multiple sclerosis. Numbness would come and go, weakness would come and go,
visual impairments would manifest themselves, and then
they would remit. Different parts of my body would experience tingling or numbness. This day in Dr. Edelson's office, three episodes of sensory loss relating to touch were
recorded.

I have a firm memory of this day because the neurologist told me that he didn't want to confirm the diagnosis

until I had some more tests, which would include a spinal fluid evaluation. At that time he was concerned about demyelination. *Myelin* is a fatty substance that surrounds the nerve fiber, forming a protective sheath. A demyelinating process involves loss of the protective myelin sheaths.

As I was leaving Dr. Edelson's office, he told me to just hold on until these various tests were done, but that he thought it might be multiple sclerosis. Never having heard of the illness in my life, I said, "What is multiple sclerosis?" I could feel myself getting upset. He was telling me something I had never heard of before, as I was about to step out the door of his office suite. He told me not to worry until after the tests, and then we would talk further.

> Although some laboratory tests have been developed, the diagnosis of MS is still based on clinical evidence. The physician must be able to show that there are two or more abnormalities (lesions) of the central nervous system (the brain and spinal cord), that these lesions predominantly involve the white matter of the brain, and that other illnesses that also produce multiple lesions have been ruled out. Depending largely on the severity and duration of the disease, these findings can vary from being extremely easy to extremely difficult to confirm.[1]

Compassion From Others

Well, I drove back to work, barely seeing for the tears. I kept thinking, "I may have multiple sclerosis, and I don't even know what it is!" When I got back to my job, I walked into my work area and burst into tears. My supervisor came to me and said, "Sharon, what did the doctor say?" I blurted out, "He said that I might have multiple sclerosis!" My supervisor was so compassionate, she took me out of the work area and calmed me down. She tried to get me to relax and not to worry until the diagnosis was confirmed. I called my husband, replayed the doctor's visit, and cried some more. He comforted me and asked whether I wanted him to come get me. I said no, that we would talk when he got home. When I got home from work, I called Mom and cried some more. Finally, John came home and we talked. Ever the lawyer, John said that we shouldn't worry about what MS is until we had a firm diagnosis and facts. So I thought positively and prepared myself for the tests scheduled for the next day. These included a second somatosensory evoked response test and a lumbar puncture to examine the spinal fluid. I was nervous about the lumbar puncture because I knew that a needle was involved, and I didn't like needles. Within a two-week time frame, the tests had been evaluated and the results given to my neurologist.

Multiple Sclerosis—First Confirmation

On June 8, 1982, John and I went in to meet with Dr. Edelson for interpretation of the results. He asked me if there had been any new symptoms since I last saw him. There were no new symptoms to report, just more numbness and continued sensory loss. The somatosensory evoked response test showed no significant changes from the one taken the previous April. However, the lumbar puncture, which analyzed spinal fluid, showed results consistent with a demyelinating process. This was the first confirmation that I had a mild form of multiple sclerosis. Dr. Edelson felt that it could go into remission, that the symptoms would go away one day and not come back. His attitude to me then was that it was not such a big deal at that time, but from that day forward my life changed.

Optic Neuritis

In August, I scheduled an appointment with my optometrist because my vision was real blurry and my left eye had pain. He referred me to an ophthalmologist because the problem was not in his area of expertise. Thus began my relationship with Dr. Harold Rodman. He was able to see me that same day, and he did all kinds of visual tests. It was determined that I had *optic*, or retrobulbar, *neuritis*. "These terms simply mean inflammation of the optic nerve and 'retrobulbar' indicates that this has affected the nerve some way behind the bulb of the eye—the eyeball."[2]

This was my first experience with this particular symptom, and it was frightening. However, optic neuritis is one of the most common eye disorders of MS.

> Optic neuritis is a frequent first symptom of multiple sclerosis. It usually begins with a loss of vision in one eye. The problem begins near the center of the visual field and spreads toward the edges. It can produce blind spots in the field of vision, blurriness, color blindness or difficulty in seeing objects either with poor contrast, or those in very bright light.[3]

It is usually treated with doses of steroids. Prednisone, a common steroid, is often prescribed as part of drug therapy treatment for multiple sclerosis.

Because this was my first occurrence of optic neuritis, the ophthalmologist thought that it probably would be temporary. "Visual symptoms—blurring, double vision, pain in the eye, or "blind spots"—also tend to be temporary and do not signify a serious course of MS."[4] Indeed, "[m]any symptoms and signs do clear partially, or even completely, following an attack."[5]

Since symptoms may be alleviated more rapidly if steroids are administered, I was prescribed a short course of oral prednisone. Usually given one month at a time, I was on a taper down regime for three weeks. "Long-term or chronic use [of prednisone] is not recommended. The drug may be taken again for brief periods if there is a recurrence or a new attack, but the effect is often less in each subsequent bout."[6] Neurologists believe that prednisone can lessen the intensity of an exacerbation—the appearance of new symptoms or an increase in the severity of existing ones—and shorten its duration. But, each individual case is different. Prednisone is not a cure for MS.

I came to know why control of salt intake is so important during the time that prednisone is being taken. One of its side effects is fluid retention and weight increase, which salt enhances. Because this was my first time to ever take prednisone, it gave me a tremendous appetite. I wanted to eat, it seemed, all the time. I stayed hungry and ate a lot of salty snacks. My husband can attest to this. As I look back at pictures taken during those early years of prednisone use, I am astounded at how fat my face and legs were. Salt certainly did its job. Prednisone also made my body tender and sore to touch. Mood swings were another side-effect. I thank God this was temporary and not permanent.

After the prescribed course, my eyesight returned completely! From that bout of optic neuritis, I gained a new appreciation for the majestic and marvelous manner in which our bodies work. I came to realize how many things we take for granted on a daily basis.

Denial

Today, I know that denial is a normal part of the acceptance process. Before acceptance is manifest, healthy denial must precede it. I just didn't want to believe that I had multiple sclerosis. I felt all right and had only experienced mild symptoms and slight pain with my optic neuritis experience. Surely a mistake had been made! I can't have multiple sclerosis. Not me. Why me? I'm only 27 years old. I've just begun a new career, a new job. I just got married. Not now!

I had so many questions that plagued me over and over again. Was I living proof concerning the proposition that, "MS strikes individuals in their most productive years, just when they are assuming major family and career responsibilities"?[7] It was like a dream. This diagnosis didn't belong to me. Did it? Here, I had a disease that there was no cure for. What kind of life did I have to look forward to? I wanted to be sure that the diagnosis was well founded. One doctor's opinion was not enough for me, I wanted three opinions.

> If a patient is reluctant to accept the diagnosis of MS, it may be best to get a second opinion as quickly as possible from another well-known authority.[8]

Second and Third Confirmations

This is exactly what I did upon leaving Dr. Edelson's office. Along with my husband, I proceeded to make appointments with neurologists associated with Georgetown University Hospital in Washington, D.C. and Johns Hopkins University Hospital in Baltimore. The Georgetown doctor agreed with the diagnosis. My third confirmation came from a neurologist at Johns Hopkins who is a leading expert and researcher in the field. After discussing my past symptoms and conducting a neurological exam, he too, agreed with the diagnosis. He said that optic neuritis is usually the "icing on the cake."

John and I had been married for one year, and we wanted to begin family planning. That was one area that was foremost in our minds. Could we have children? What effect does pregnancy have on multiple sclerosis? Is multiple sclerosis hereditary? We asked these questions and other questions of the Johns Hopkins neurologist. His compassion, advice, and patience were so reassuring to us. He encouraged me to cross bridges as I encountered them. He told me that I could have children and multiple sclerosis is not hereditary. He said that I would have no problems with multiple sclerosis during the pregnancy, but most likely would experience an exacerbation period after the baby was born due to the change in my routine schedule. It would be more demanding with late night and early morning feedings, the attention required by the baby during the day, etc. Because of the lack of sleep associated with child care, my body would be fatigued and I would need extended periods of rest. I really appreciated the neurologist's calming manner. He helped me place the confirmation of the diagnosis into proper perspective. When we left Johns Hopkins, I had new insight regarding multiple sclerosis and a determination to take one day at a time.

Acceptance

Acceptance of anything is a process, one that evolves with time. Three years after my confirmed diagnosis, I found a ten-point checklist that proved useful for gauging the extent of my growth in accepting the fact that I had a condition known as multiple sclerosis. It has been a blessing and here it is:

1. MS is no longer the focus of your life.

2. Depression, anger, and bitterness are occasional emotions, not the way of life.

3. Although you are optimistic, you accept that you may have either a mild or more progressive course in the future.

4. You continue to make plans for the future, with the understanding that they may need to be altered.

5. In the event of physical impairment, you are able to readjust goals in work, leisure-time activities, and relationships to match ability.

6. You are no longer fearful of the future.

7. You are willing to accept help from others graciously while finding your own way to reciprocate.

8. Regardless of physical limitations, you maintain a positive self-image.

9. You follow good health practices and avoid tempting fate with aggravating factors.

10. You view MS as an added burden in your life, not the reason for all your problems.[9]

Yes, I had received confirmation of the multiple sclerosis diagnosis, but it would not become real until my routines changed.

After the appointment at Johns Hopkins, I knew that I had to gather data about multiple sclerosis so I would be educated about the disease—a disease that was a part of me now. Nonetheless, I wasn't in a hurry to gather the information. I didn't feel the need to call the Multiple Sclerosis Society yet. I still felt like this disease was distant from me. I went through the "what did I do to deserve this" phase. I still felt like the same person, although weakness and other motor symptoms were beginning to manifest themselves. I didn't want to have multiple sclerosis.

My sister Kaye was more interested in gathering literature on MS than I was. She secured books, tapes, and anything else she could get her hands on. I just wasn't ready to get into all that at that point in my life. I wanted to go on performing my usual routines. I did not want to be overwhelmed by this new knowledge.

I had a loving husband who was there to comfort, support, and encourage me. I had a family who cared and was very supportive. God had blessed me with friends who listened and cared. There was even compassion at my workplace. Members of my home church where I had gotten married were praying for me. Yet, I yearned for fellowship with the saints of God so I could focus on His agenda and not my own. I desired a positive, spiritual mind-set, not a negative one. John and I weren't members of a church in our area. When we went to church, we would go back to my home church in Columbia, thinking time would resolve the issue. We started visiting various churches and finally joined Canaan Baptist Church in Washington, D.C. in March of 1983. The ministry I joined was the M. Cecil Mills Ensemble, an adult gospel choir. John joined the male usher board.

Being involved with the choir kept me from becoming totally preoccupied with my condition. However, every time some physical symptom like numbness, weakness, blurriness, vision impairment, tripping while walking, or bumping into walls and corners occurred, I was confronted with the reality of my diagnosis. The value of just being able to do things we take for granted—like brushing our teeth, washing our face, tying a shoe—took on a new meaning for me. I developed a deeper compassion and appreciation for disabled people and other persons afflicted with illness as I began to deal with my own weaknesses.

The effects of optic neuritis on my vision became a major focal point during this early period. I would have short exacerbation periods and then go into remission. I loved my remission times. Fluorescent lighting was something I had to deal with because my work environment was saturated with it, and it affected my eyes. The grocery store has it, retail stores have it, schools have it, and many other places are lighted with fluorescent lights. It's amazing what you begin to notice when something has a significant impact on your day-to-day activities.

My neurologist recommended that I speak with one of their counselors to discuss my feelings about being diagnosed with MS. I felt that I didn't need to because I wasn't depressed about the news and felt I could deal with it. Yet I went to see the counselor anyway. It seemed as if she *wanted* me to feel down and out about the diagnosis, that I was supposed to feel angry and upset. However, I just didn't feel that way. Those were emotional responses I neither had nor needed at the time. As I left her office, I felt I had wasted my time. I was strong and clear in my mind that multiple sclerosis would require "a determined spirit." However, when my sister Virginia said to me rather flippantly one day, "Oh, Sharon, you won't die from it," that was the best jolt I could have received during this acceptance stage.

Chapter 6

What Is Multiple Sclerosis?

The heart of the prudent acquires knowledge, and the ear of the wise seeks knowledge.
Proverbs 18:15

During my acceptance period I gathered information on multiple sclerosis. I needed a definition and overview of it. I wanted to know what the clinical picture was. In order to understand the symptoms occurring in my body as well as various terminology associated with the disease, I sought answers. The responsibility was mine to become an educated patient. I truly did not know very much about the disease. What I knew was vague and undetailed. It could have been measured with a teaspoon. I needed insight so I would recognize physical signs and symptoms as they occurred. I wanted to know within myself what MS was. Yes, I was the one with MS, but the knowledge about it would not only affect me, but my family, friends, and others I would come in contact with. I wanted to be able to answer the question "What is Multiple Sclerosis?"

In writing this book, I felt it would be important for the reader to know more than, "MS is a disease." Accordingly, I read books, pamphlets, and other materials concerning multiple sclerosis in order to provide readers with basic facts about the disease. Researching and acquiring knowledge on the subject was a blessing for me. Granted, I had read many things after my confirmed diagnosis, but nothing like I've read in preparing and writing this chapter.

Multiple Sclerosis is a disease of the central nervous system that interferes with the brain's ability to control such functions as walking, talking, seeing, etc. It is a relatively common, progressively disabling disease with its onset in early adult life. "There is a definite sex predilection, with the majority of cases occurring in females. Various studies have reported that 55 to 80% of the patients are women."[1] The *multiple* part means two things: (a) many scattered areas of the brain and spinal cord are affected by the disease, and (b) the disease's symptoms can be mild or severe and they come and go unpredictably. The *sclerosis* part means that the disease involves *sclerosed,* or hardened, tissue in damaged areas of the brain and spinal cord. MS is not preventable and there is no cure for it to date. It is not a mental illness nor is it contagious.

It became apparent very quickly that I needed an elementary knowledge of the anatomy of the *central nervous system* (CNS), the place where the disease manifests itself. The CNS consists of the brain and the spinal cord. The brain is in the cranial cavity—the skull—and the spinal cord runs down the center of the spinal column—the backbone.

How MS Affects the CNS

The central nervous system acts like a switchboard, sending electrical messages along the nerves to various parts of the body. These messages control all our conscious and unconscious movements. Most healthy nerve fibers are insulated by myelin, a fatty substance that aids the flow of messages. In MS, the myelin breaks down and is replaced by scar tissue, which distorts or even blocks the flow of messages. "Demyelination can slow down or even block the flow of signals from the central nervous system to the rest of the body impairing such functions as vision, strength or coordination."[2]

What Causes Multiple Sclerosis?

The cause of MS is a big mystery. "No one knows what actually causes MS, but we do know that it is an acquired disease—you are not born with it."[3] I found that scientists have three basic theories concerning the disease:

"1. The virus attack theory, MS might be caused by some slow-acting viruses, or might be a delayed reaction to a common virus.

"2. The immune reaction theory, MS might involve an autoimmune reaction in which the body attacks its own tissues by mistake.

"3. The combination theory, the body defense system might become confused because some viruses take over parts of cells and it might attack both host cells and virus."[4]

A publication distributed by the National Multiple Sclerosis Society states, "[i]n summary, it seems very likely that the initial event that starts MS is a viral infection, but the autoimmune process is what keeps MS going."[5]

Symptoms of MS

Symptoms vary greatly from person to person, and from time to time, they can vary in the same person. They vary according to the area of the nervous system that is affected. For many, MS involves a series of attacks—exacerbations—and partial or complete recoveries—remissions. "The initial and later symptoms of MS are of four general types: motor (movement) 35%, sensory (touch) 35%, visual 20%, and other (bladder, bowel, mental, etc.) 10%."[6] Motor symptoms consist of the following: weakness, spasticity, ataxia, and speech disorder. Sensory symptoms consist of the following: numbness and pain. Visual symptoms include blurred vision (optic neuritis) and double vision. Other symptoms that can occur are: dizziness, deafness, urinary symptoms, bowel problems, sexual problems, energy problems, and mental symptoms. Some examples of symptoms are: tingling, impaired sensation, lack of coordination, disturbances in equilibrium, involuntary, rapid movement of the eyes, slurred speech, tremors, stiffness in legs, and weakness of limbs. In more severe cases, symptoms may include paralysis of the extremities, impaired bladder and bowel function, fatigue, and lack of energy.

Course of MS

The kind of course MS will take is unpredictable.

"The patterns of the disease usually seen are:

"(a) Benign form, with few, mild early attacks (medical term—"exacerbations") and complete or nearly complete clearing (medical term—"remissions"). The patient has a normal life expectancy and minimal or no disability. About 20% of cases fall into this category.

"(b) Exacerbating-remitting form, with more frequent, early attacks and less complete clearing but showing long periods of stability. Some degree of disability is usually present. About 25% of cases follow this pattern.

"(c) Chronic-relapsing form, with fewer and less-complete remissions after attacks. The disability is cumulative and greater than seen in the previous forms. The course may run for many years and then plateau with moderate to severe disability. About 40% of cases are of this type.

"(d) Chronic-progressive form, which is similar to the previous form except the onset is more insidious, and the course is slowly progressive without remissions. About 15% of all cases follow this pattern."[7]

I have found this "course" information to be very useful, because with it I have been able to track how my MS has changed in the 13 years since my diagnosis.

Confirmation of MS

There are two basic signs to confirm multiple sclerosis: signs of nervous system damage and the come-and-go pattern of the disease. With regard to the first, numbness or tingling of hands and feet, unexplained weakness, or paralysis may be prevalent. At least two parts of the nervous system must be involved. Concerning the second sign, the symptoms of MS usually appear and disappear without warning.

Treatment of MS

There is currently no cure for multiple sclerosis. However, the following things can be done to help an individual with MS remain independent, comfortable, and productive: overall health maintenance, people with MS need to stay active, eat a nutritious diet, and get adequate rest to feel good and keep their resistance up; physical therapy, exercise programs and muscle retraining may help patients recovering from acute attacks and can relieve tightening in muscles; psychotherapy and counseling, individual and group therapy may assist patients and families in coping with depression, anxiety, and limitations caused by MS (this is important because the uncertainty about how long periods of remission will last may make adjustment to this disease particularly difficult); medication, drugs usually are used primarily to relieve specific symptoms, and can be used to help reduce frequency, severity, and duration of acute exacerbations.

Chapter 7

A Determined Spirit

Being confident of this very thing, that He who has begun
a good work in you will complete it....

Philippians 1:6

Now that I had the facts about multiple sclerosis, how was I going to equip myself mentally to deal with what I had to face? I sought the matters of God, spiritual issues like faith, hope, and love. I knew that my heavenly Father could handle anything. I was ready to learn how He was going to work with me, for God is bigger than me or multiple sclerosis.

Between receiving the third confirmation of the diagnosis, obtaining data about multiple sclerosis, and becoming pregnant with my first child in October 1982, I really got to focus on my faith and my relationship with God. Where was I in my walk with the Lord? I wanted to know God's purpose for me in this life. How did Philippians 1:29, "For to you it has been granted on behalf of Christ, not only to believe in Him, but also to suffer for His sake," apply to me? If I was created in His image, how could I have multiple sclerosis? I didn't understand. I was confused! After gaining a clearer understanding of MS from my collection of data, I felt overwhelmed. I knew that I had to develop a new strategy for coping. I didn't want fear to be my greatest crippler. I knew I couldn't rely on my strength alone. I decided to simply trust God. The stage was set for "*A Determined Spirit.*" Focusing on the Lord rather than circumstances was the road "a determined spirit" was about to travel. But it would not be until 1994 that an understanding of God's purpose for my having MS became crystal clear.

What is "a determined spirit"? It is a person who allows the Word of God to strengthen their faith, which is necessary for enduring trials or tribulations. It is a person who will accept the challenge of taking God at His Word, which is faith's foundation. Because He said it, you must now believe it.

What are the attributes of "a determined spirit"? First and foremost, it is a believer's steadfast, unfaltering, and unwavering faith in the promises of God. It is that inner spirit that is developed when one experiences the trials and tribulations referred to in the Book of James. It is the confidence the three Hebrew boys had in the fiery furnace; the steadfastness of Job; the endurance of the apostle Paul. "A determined spirit" is submission to the Holy Spirit that results from an understanding of our relationship with God.

What is the function of "a determined spirit"?

1. To inspire and temper thoughts, feelings, or actions;

2. To be an overcomer;

3. To search the Scriptures and find God's promises concerning a trial or tribulation, and then to exercise faith and obedience with regard to God's Word.

To carry out the functions, one must focus on the Word of God. Below are Scriptures for each numbered function that have helped me:

1. Philippians 4:8, "…whatever things are true, whatever things are noble, whatever things are just, whatever things are pure, whatever things are lovely, whatever things are of good report…meditate on these things."

2. Second Corinthians 12:10, "…I take pleasure in infirmities, in reproaches, in needs, in persecutions, in distresses, for Christ's sake. For when I am weak, then I am strong."

3. Proverbs 4:20-22, "My son, give attention to my words; incline your ear to my sayings. Do not let them depart from your eyes; keep them in the midst of your heart; for they are life to those who find them, and health to all their flesh."

I had always considered myself a strong person, with the attitude that I could make it no matter what occurred. I came to realize that in my struggle with multiple sclerosis, I needed to develop a closer relationship with God. I began a process of wanting to know Him. I desired spiritual growth. I wanted to know His attributes and His function. At that time in my life, I just knew He was part of the Trinity, the Godhead. That was it! I didn't realize that everything I was to face would be His job to handle. Multiple sclerosis was to be the catalyst that would humble me and cause me to rededicate my life to God. I was to become an instrument for His use and bring glory to Him through my struggles. What a realization!

I had to stop and evaluate what my relationship with God had been, but I also needed to learn more about what it would become in Christ. Focus shifted from self-will to God's will. I was His child, and I knew no matter what, He would take care of me. I just didn't know how much! I came to understand more fully that every believer has the Holy Spirit living on the inside of him or her. Yes, I'm a believer! Therefore, I not only have "a determined spirit" inside of me, but the Holy Spirit too; and He is alive and active. With God leading and my mind to be transformed, submissive, and controlled by Him, what an awesome development took place by my obedience.

"A determined spirit" presses on even when it seems there's no more energy left, no more strength left, no more wind behind the sails. God is always there to send another wind, to strengthen, encourage, revitalize, and give another dose of perseverance. "A determined spirit" is a light ever shining, glorifying God. Its purpose is to stay in the race, fight the good fight, be content in whatever the situation is, and remain steadfast despite the circumstances. My mind was made up to submit to this spirit. It didn't happen all at once. It's an ongoing process.

"A determined spirit" has the confidence to make it through a rough time, through the roller coaster ride of symptoms, through exacerbations, treatments, doctor's visits, through whatever comes. It doesn't allow you to focus on what you're going through. Instead you focus on the knowledge that you will get through it. "Many are the afflictions of the righteous, but the Lord delivers him out of them all" (Ps. 34:19) is one of God's promises that I hold on to.

"A determined spirit" requires that you exercise your faith and believe Scripture, such as First Peter 2:24, which says, "Who Himself bore our sins in His own body on the tree, that we, having died to sins, might live for righteousness—by whose stripes you were healed." You must not doubt that the outcome has already been taken care of by God. Faith is calling those things that are not as though they were (see Rom. 4:17). "Now faith is the substance of things hoped for, the evidence of things not seen" (Heb. 11:1). It is believing something to be even though you may not see it.

The Word of God has been the cornerstone of my development as "a determined spirit." I am "...increasing in the knowledge of God; strengthened with all might, according to His glorious power..." (Col. 1:10-11). There have also been special people in my life who have helped influence my present state as "a determined spirit." These people include my husband and children, my parents, my brothers and sisters—Rebecca, Silas Jr., Virginia, Dwight, and Kaye—my cousin Carmen, my friends, the saints of God, my doctors, and various pastors from my church experiences. Their influences will be highlighted further on in this book.

"A determined spirit" is a must! It shapes and molds the mind-set necessary to endure trials and tribulations. It urges us to study God's Word and learn how to listen to His voice to receive the knowledge, wisdom, and strength that only He so graciously and abundantly provides.

Chapter 8

Pregnancy and Multiple Sclerosis

Behold, children are a heritage from the Lord, the fruit of the womb is His reward.

Psalm 127:3

"A determined spirit" was contemplating pregnancy and childbirth. After my consultation with the Johns Hopkins neurologist, I made further inquiries regarding the effect of MS on these important decisions. I was greatly encouraged by the following medical finding:

"The decision of whether to have children is a very personal one. There is no medical reason why an adult with MS should not become a parent. There is no evidence the MS causes any problems for the unborn or newborn child. The disease cannot be transmitted to the baby. In addition, there is very little evidence that the stress of childbirth has any lasting effects on the disease. Each couple must evaluate for themselves their feelings about childbearing and their ability to raise a child should the disability become severe."[1]

Many of the brochures and books that I read agreed—concluding that most studies have not shown pregnancy to have had any effect on the long-term course of multiple sclerosis. While some early studies revealed an increase in the frequency of exacerbations in the first three to six months after the birth of a baby, "[t]his increase in incidence is not necessarily due to the pregnancy but more likely to the physical exertion involved in caring for a newborn."[2] To know that pregnancy was not inherently out of the question was great news!

But, there were other considerations that had to be taken into account regarding the decision to have children. Did I have the stamina to care for a baby and then an active child? What were the prospects of hiring someone to help me with child care if that became necessary? Were there family and friends I could call on if I needed help? These were considerations, but I was not discouraged. "A determined spirit" puts your mind at rest and gives you courage and peace, and that's what I was—determined. It did not matter what I had to go through, I wanted to try. I knew that God promised never to leave me nor forsake me (see Heb. 13:5), so I was already taken care of. I really looked forward to the experience. It wasn't the challenge of just birthing a child; it was also moving to the next plateau in our marriage, parenthood. I knew the final decision rested with God, for it was His timetable, not ours. I was buttressed by His Word that instructs us to "be fruitful and multiply" (Gen. 1:22). Time revealed His will to bring forth fruit of my womb on June 9, 1983 and August 14, 1985 with the birth of our daughters, Stacey Renée and Ashley Revée.

Baby Girl Stacey

Having discussed MS and family planning with my doctor, John and I were ready to try. I wanted two children.

My heart's desire was for a daughter because I was most familiar with girls, having grown up with three sisters who had combed and braided my hair. I wanted a girl who I could dress up in pretty dresses and patent leather shoes and whose hair I could comb. I even had a name already, Stacey. John wasn't particular about the sex of the child. He was just excited about being a father and ready to get started. So begin we did! My cycle was never late. But, when it finally didn't come at the appointed time in October 1982, I suspected that the Lord had answered our prayers. I was so excited that I went out and got a home pregnancy test before I went to my gynecologist. It was positive. I then made an appointment and went to my doctor. Sure enough, I was pregnant! John and I were thrilled.

The MS went into remission during the entire pregnancy, so I had no problems carrying the baby. My obstetrician was well informed about my MS status and talked to us about the possibility of having a caesarean in the event that my uterus didn't fully dilate in a timely manner. Wouldn't you know that one of the childbirth classes I attended dealt with caesarean delivery. I didn't pay a lot of attention in that class since John was away, traveling because of his job, and I figured there was no need for me to listen. Little did I know!

I was given a baby shower at work and took leave for six months. I came home a month before the baby was due so that I could rest, store up energy, and prepare the nursery. One day while coming down the steps, I slipped and fell. It scared me. I was concerned about the baby, but I went to the doctor and everything was fine.

I got up the morning of June 8, 1983, and felt like I was having cramps. I thought to myself, *Not today!* It was my nephew Garrett's birthday, and I really did not want my baby born on a relative's birthday. However, when I went to the bathroom, I discovered that I had passed my mucus plug and the labor process had begun. John called the doctor, who advised us to go to the hospital. My suitcase was packed, so we got dressed and hurried to the Washington Hospital Center. It was 5:10 a.m. Once there, I was checked in, wheeled into a labor room, and dressed in my hospital attire by 5:20 a.m. Two doctors had attended me during this pregnancy, Dr. Sewell and Dr. Clark. Dr. Sewell, my main doctor, arrived and examined me at 5:40 a.m. I was 90% effaced and had dilated only one centimeter. At 5:50 a.m., I was put on the fetal monitor. At 6:38 a.m., I was put on a glucose IV and various other prep things were done, including blood being drawn. I napped off and on.

At 8:15 a.m., Dr. Sewell returned and broke my water. The timing of contractions, as well as breathing instructions, were started by my coach, my husband. Dressed in the requisite hospital garb, John also began to document everything that occurred and the time it took place. Thank you, John, for being so helpful and observant.

Dr. Clark and a nurse checked on me at 1:20 p.m. When he returned at 3:10 p.m., I was only 2-3 centimeters dilated. Both John and I were saying, "come on, baby"! At 3:59 p.m., the baby must have said, "get that urine out of my way," because I had to use the bedpan.

Dr. Clark returned at 4:19 p.m. and I had dilated 4-5 centimeters. John wrote in his notes, "baby in two hours?"

But it was not to be. The doctor said that when I reached 5 centimeters, I could be given an epidural to ease the pain. At 5:00 p.m. John was sitting on my bed saying, "come on little fellow!" I was examined by Dr. Clark at 5:20 p.m. and had dilated 5 centimeters. He left instructions for me to receive an epidural. Well at 5:48 p.m. no one had come to give me one and I was having hard labor pains. Every time a big contraction occurred, John would say, "Breathe, Sharon, breathe." "Dr. Moore" (John) took matters into his own hands and asked a nurse about the epidural that had been ordered. I just wanted to go home! I begged John to take me home and he told me, "Sharon, you can't go home now, the baby is coming. Hang in there!"

I received the epidural at 6:52 p.m. It only eased the pain for a couple of hours, for I had others at 8:45 p.m., 11:30 p.m., and 2:00 a.m. By the last one, I was 90% effaced and had dilated 7 centimeters. We waited, waited, and waited. Dr. Sewell returned at 3:10 a.m. and said I would have to have a cesarean (C-section). At that point I didn't care. That was my deliverance, the answer to my prayer!

Prepping for the "C" was done at 3:50 a.m. Finally, at 5:50 a.m. on June 9, more than 12 hours after the "two hours" mentioned before by Dr. Clark, a caesarean was performed and Stacey Renée was born. She weighed 8 lbs. 4 ozs. and was very healthy. Hallelujah! Birthing a child is truly a miracle.

The entire labor process had drained my energy. I was whipped! I ran a fever and was given a glucose IV. I was supposed to have "rooming in" with the baby, but since I had a fever, for the first two days they brought Stacey in for feeding and then took her back to the nursery. Finally, by day three I ran no fever and she was able to stay in the nursery in my room. Five days later, we went home. Thank you, Lord!

As soon as we came home with Baby Stacey, I started coming out of remission. The surgery took a lot out of me, the healing process was slow, and the weather was hot. As I would later learn, heat is a foe of my MS. I breast-fed Stacey. That was a draining task for me; but since it was healthy for her, it was a labor of love. During these early days, it was crucial that I rest as much as possible, do only what was absolutely necessary, ask for help when needed, and stay in an air-conditioned, cool environment.

When Stacey was three months old, we had her blessed at Canaan Baptist Church, the church we were affiliated with. What a lovely day that was. Children are a gift from God, so we wanted to give her back to Him—realizing that she had been entrusted to us for care and training. At five months, John and I left Stacey in the care of my parents and went with another couple to vacation in Acapulco, Mexico. I'm so glad we did. We missed her, but we had a great time!

December passed too quickly. I was to return to work in January. I would be going to a new location. The environment I would be entering was very unsettled due to the fact that reorganization was under way. The company had split, and people had been relocated all over the place while I was on leave. However, change (an element of life, the timing of which we often can't control) was certainly not new to me. I had already experienced many changes and others were in store.

Baby Girl Ashley

I was finally going into remission following Stacey's birth and infant care when I learned that I was pregnant with Ashley. It was December 1984. I was out of sorts for a little while because I was just back to normal and feeling strong. I didn't want to come out of remission and go back through what I had just experienced. I didn't! I didn't look forward to it at all. I kept wondering, *how did I get pregnant?* I had used birth control. Remembering that God was in control, I realized that being concerned about being pregnant was not the right attitude. It wasn't good for me or the baby, so "a determined spirit" regrouped.

The responsibilities of being a wife, mothering an 18-month old, and active involvement in the church choir drained my energy reservoir. God prepared me to meet those commitments and I learned to program myself to rest and not rush.

It was about this time, during the spring of 1985, that John and I purchased a vacation home in West Virginia with my sister and her husband. A contemporary one-level home with high ceilings, it was located at a resort called "The Woods" and situated on a 1 1/2 acre wooded lot. We staked a wooden sign with the cabin's name, "Rushless," at the end of the driveway. It became a place to get away from it all. "Rushless" had access to all the recreational facilities of the resort, including swimming pools, tennis courts, a fitness center, and indoor sports. It was about an hour and 45 minute drive from Washington, and the drive was beautiful. The house was finished during my pregnancy with Ashley. I looked forward to utilizing it after she was born, so that I could continue to rest and not rush.

I returned to my neurologist's office on May 13, 1985. I was six months pregnant and still had symptoms related to my vision. Fluorescent lights presented significant problems for me in buildings, retail stores, and grocery stores especially. Whenever I was exposed to these lights, they seemed to eat right through my eyes. It was something else! I was unable to read for more than a half hour. Fortunately, during this visit I had no recurrence of numbness, my gait was normal, and routine coordination tests went well. Dr. Edelson told me that at the conclusion of the pregnancy he wanted to repeat a visual response test and have a magnetic resonance imaging scan performed to further define my MS.

During the month of May, John and I decided to take a little vacation to Paradise Island in the Bahamas. We both needed it, and in June, pregnant and all, we went. At that time in my life, I could still go to hot climate areas and was able to walk long distances, swim, sunbathe and enjoy myself. I remained in remission until after Ashley was born. Praise God!

It was August 13, 1985, and I was driving home from Mom's house with Stacey and my niece Kia. I was tired and felt like I was having cramps. I said to myself, "I think I'm having contractions." When I got home I told John that I felt like I was having contractions, but they were far apart. It was about 10:00 p.m. John started timing them and said, "Let's wait until the morning, and I'll take you to the hospital." Well, that's what we did. However, I was having a caesarean and could have gone to the hospital the night before. As it turned out, all of the operating rooms were occupied, so I had to wait all day anyway, going through the labor pains and breathing exercises. I was mad at John! Finally, we got an operating room, and Ashley Revée was born by caesarean at 6:19 p.m. Weighing 7 lbs. 13 ozs., she was healthy and hungry. Ashley had a head full of hair. No wonder my hair hadn't grown much during my pregnancy with her—she took it all! I wasn't too wiped out from the surgery, so I was able to nurse her the first night.

My oldest sister Becky was keeping Stacey. I had spoken with her on the phone, and she was crying to see me. I had my sister bring Stacey to see us in the "sibling room"; we had rolled Ashley there in her "rooming in" bed. When Stacey saw me, she wanted to get in my lap. There were tears of joy in the room that day. Stacey had this look of amazement on her face as she peered into her sister's face. So many thoughts were occurring in my mind, John's, and Stacey's. Wow! What a time that was. Stacey cried when she had to leave, but I assured her that we would be home soon. I thanked God for my family and just looked forward to being at home.

I didn't run a fever and felt better than I had the first time. I got to go home in three days. I was so happy! Ashley's godmother-to-be, Debra, sent a yellow dress with a bonnet for her to wear home. John came that morning. We dressed Ashley, I dressed, and home we went!

My mom came over and stayed with us for a time. I needed all the help I could get. What a blessing she was!

Again it was crucial for me to rest and stay in the air conditioning. I went up and down the steps as infrequently as I could.

When Ashley was four months old, we had her blessed at my home church, First Baptist Church of Guilford. What a lovely day that was. I had taken a leave of absence from the choir during my second trimester, but returned after Ashley's blessing. Choir rehearsals, commitments, and engagements resumed as part of my life's activities. I enjoyed singing for the glory of the Lord and honored my commitments. Stacey went with me to choir rehearsals, while Ashley stayed with John.

Chapter 9

Working, a Struggle

The Lord is my rock and my fortress and my deliverer; my God, my strength, in whom will I trust.

Psalm 18:2

After Stacey was born, I returned to C&P as a business office supervisor in January 1984. Each morning I got up early, fed and dressed Stacey, fed and dressed myself, dropped her off at the babysitter, and continued on to my job. John was not a breakfast person so I didn't have to prepare anything for him. Stacey was a good baby. She wasn't fussy and would go to anyone. I had no problems picking her up or carrying her, even though she was heavy. I was able to meet her needs with the help of God, my husband, and other family and friends. That was a blessing!

The work environment was busy from the time I arrived at my cubicle until I went home. I had to get acclimated to the organizational changes that had occurred while I was on leave. There were a lot of meetings. I supervised a new group that I had to get to know, train, and evaluate. Although I didn't like having to take the weight for the group's inability to achieve its goals because of the work habits of a few individuals, that's the responsibility of a supervisor. Most of the employees were earnest workers, but there's always one who tests you. Overall, I came to realize that my group was understanding and supportive of what I was going through with MS.

Now was not the time for an "out of remission" period—an exacerbation—but here it was. Soon after I returned to work, I became fatigued because of the MS. My vision was blurred, but my eyes didn't hurt as they had in August of 1982. The acuity of my left eye was worse than that of the right eye. It was difficult to see in daylight and office light; the fluorescent lights at my job site were extremely bothersome. Again, it was as though the lighting ate right through my eye and went straight to the nerves, affecting the clarity of my vision. It was very worrisome and irritating. In contrast, in the night light and household lighting I could see almost normal. I just kept thinking, *What is going on with my eyes?* Sometimes I would be at my desk and think, *What am I doing here, I really can't see.* After a moment of prayer, "a determined spirit" would rise to the occasion and provide me with the boost of energy I needed to complete the job agenda for the day. I had to go back to the ophthalmologist on January 9, and I was again put on a prednisone taper-down treatment course.

About this point in my life, I decided to buy a journal to regularly document my thoughts and feelings concerning daily events. This entry was written during that bout with optic neuritis:

I am trying to be strong and patient, but I become aggravated and depressed sometimes. I believe in

God and I know He'll get me through this, as He has many times before. I pray daily for strength, and I pray that He will heal my body. My ophthalmologist has had me on prednisone for a week now. I am waiting to hear from him after he confers with my neurologist. I still can't help but ask, "Why me?" I'm a good person, I've tried to do things the right way. I'm not perfect, and I've made mistakes. Why must I suffer with this disease?

This entry was dated January 18, 1984, a few weeks after I returned to work, and it was just the beginning of many journal entries that would record medical aspects of my MS experiences.

One day the weather was inclement, and I could hardly see to drive to work. I turned around, went back home, and called in to the office to say that I just couldn't make it. I saw Dr. Edelson on February 14. It was my fourth bout with visual impairment. My acuity had not yet returned to normal from the optic neuritis in January. My coordination and walking were normal, even though I was experiencing numbness in my left leg and weakness in the right leg. "A determined spirit" said, "keep pressing on."

I was on sick leave from March 5, 1984 to March 16, 1984, due to the effect of the optic neuritis. My general physical state was one of extreme fatigue and weakness. I was also experiencing other physical ailments. I was communicating a lot with my general practitioner, and I felt like I was just falling apart. In May, I had an appointment with Dr. Wilkinson and was placed on sick leave. In July of 1984, I left my management job on permanent disability. Wow! Things had happened so fast.

In October, 1984, I saw Dr. Edelson again. I seemed to be visiting his office quite frequently. My left eye had not returned to normal from the last optic neuritis bout in March. I was still experiencing blurriness. I didn't have problems with the steroids, but I hadn't improved much either. I was not defeated; "a determined spirit" kept me focused and I learned to take one day at a time.

I thank God for providing me with the employment opportunities that I've had and for sustaining me as I have sought to provide good and faithful service despite the struggle.

Balloon Creations

Even though working was a struggle, I held fast to the dream of owning my own business—a dream I had nurtured since graduating from college. I'd taken business classes in graduate school, and accounting courses. Prior to going to work at the telephone company, I used to sell art part time. I did well, but I still yearned to be owner of my own business. I wanted to be an entrepreneur. That business desire was inside of me.

I started attending classes at Howard University dealing with small businesses and classes offered by the Small Business Administration on "How to Start A Small Business," as well as other applicable classes. Once again I was excited and motivated. I started researching the balloon business. I wanted to be involved in a business that sent the message of joy. A balloon business seemed ideal.

I talked with Ashley's godmother about becoming a partner with me in this endeavor. Debra quickly said yes and we went to work on a business plan. She purchased an

Entrepreneur magazine that listed and sold comprehensive manuals on any kind of business you wanted to know about. We ordered a balloon manual, which provided start up costs, income projections, and information concerning other aspects of the balloon business. The manual was excellent! We went out and talked with others in the balloon business, none of whom provided any negative feedback. They were more than willing to answer questions, explain various marketing techniques, provide referrals for purchasing inventory, and share other useful tips. It really was a blessing.

I wanted the business to be home-based, and we discovered that was okay as well. I discussed the idea with my husband and he was all in favor of it. John has always encouraged me to reach for my dreams. Success or failure, he has always been supportive. The idea was getting better and better. Finally, the decision was made and "Balloon Creations," a balloon delivery service, was born. Here is the entry I wrote in my journal on April 5, 1984:

> I'm on the up and up. I can see again and have been doing so for two weeks. Thanks be to God. I'm involved in a busy venture, Balloon Creations.

John had the rarely-used porch, which stretched across the front of our house, converted into a workshop, and Balloon Creations had its grand opening on May 5, 1984. We had a grand time, with free balloons, refreshments, and a clown to entertain the kids. I had a great partner and lots of support. We were on our way!

Balloon Creations was open every day of the week except Sunday. We didn't want Sunday business because we were committed to being in worship and to other church obligations. On rare occasions, we accepted a Sunday job for a special client, either very early before church or after church. My partner and I did a lot of decorating jobs on weekends, including bouquet deliveries. Valentine's Day and Mother's Day were our busiest holidays. The business was able to pay its expenses, purchase a delivery van, spread lots of joy, and turn a profit. We even went for balloon decorating training in Harrisburg, Pennsylvania, at one of the largest balloon companies in the business. That was a very exciting day.

I loved Balloon Creations. I was proud because it was the realization of a long-held goal. The business brought so much joy to so many people. It had a great clientele, serving not only the needs of adults but children as well. We did costumed deliveries upon request and even had a gift that could be mailed anywhere in the United States, called the "balloon-in-a-box." Recognizing that God is the giver of all gifts, His spirit prevailed in whatever we did. By His grace, Balloon Creations was a success!

After three years, Balloon Creations came to a close in June 1988, and the inventory was sold. With the increased demands of growing daughters and MS flare ups, it simply got to be too much for me. The experience of operating Balloon Creations was a testament to "a determined spirit." Balloon Creations' purpose had been served and its season was over.

We retained the van that had been purchased for the business in May 1985. We had it converted from a cargo van into a passenger van in June 1988, and that fall I got handicapped tags. The van—affectionately named "BC"—has really been a blessing. As I write, BC has not yet been retired. Thank God!

Chapter 10

The Need for Other Professionals

And you will seek Me and find Me, when you search for Me with all your heart.

Jeremiah 29:13

More Doctor Visits

Life was progressing. I was 31 years old, married, and the mother of two children. A lot had transpired in four years. I thought I knew what fatigue was when I had just one child. Well, with two children it seemed that I was in that state all the time. I simply had no energy by noon everyday. A daily nap became mandatory. I found that with a nap I had a little more energy with which to function.

I came out of remission in December 1985 and was put on prednisone. I was scheduled for an MRI (magnetic resonance imaging) test to determine the progression pattern of my MS. I saw the neurologist on January 7, 1986, and was given the results of the MRI (which provides pictures of the central nervous system). I had a typical pattern of MS, but it was still evaluated as mild. I was experiencing visual difficulty in the left eye and some gait unsteadiness.

When I left Dr. Edelson's office, the prognosis was that I was doing well and would not have to see him for a year unless there was a problem.

As it happened, I was in one doctor's office or another throughout early 1986. At times the MS seemed to trigger other ailments. In February 1986, I went to my general practitioner. I was having lower right abdominal pain, the right side of my body was numb, and there was some pain in my right leg. I was given a prescription for the pain. I began to think, *I've just finished the prednisone, and now I have another medicine to take.*

On March 18, 1986, I returned to Dr. Edelson. Since February, I had been having numbness and weakness in my right leg, and it seemed to be getting worse. I was walking with a limp and my right leg was dragging. I was given another course of prednisone. An experimental drug called Cytoxin was mentioned to me, but I had no interest in the drug. I was no guinea pig and wouldn't submit to an experimental drug.

On May 20, 1986, I returned to Dr. Edelson. I was doing rather well even though I had numbness in my right leg, blurriness in my vision, fatigue, and a constipation problem. My gait was slightly wide-based and slightly stiff. I was experiencing spasticity in my legs, which was a feeling of tightness and stiffness. Otherwise I was basically all right. The plan was for me to stay off steroids. I asked Dr. Edelson, "Will my fingers always be numb?" He explained the principle of residua. This is when MS strikes the same areas, leaves damage, and you don't return completely to baseline. An example is the numbness in my fingertips.

With each new attack, I am left with some increasing residua. Dr. Edelson recommended that I talk to a physical
therapist and a nurse practitioner, so I left his office with
appointments having been scheduled for me. It was good
to know that I could seek help from other professionals. I
was to see Dr. Edelson in six months if nothing occurred
beforehand. Even back then, it seemed that I was fine in
his office, but as soon as I got home symptoms would
manifest if they had not been there before, or they would
worsen. However, I refused to turn around and call him;
"a determined spirit" would just press on.

Physical Therapy

Physical therapy was a welcome referral. As an option
to be used in the treatment process, its objective is to pre-
serve and enhance the condition of the body through appropriate exercise.

"[Physical therapy] may be helpful for some MS patients during certain phases of the disease. While by
no means curative, it can help patients make the
best possible use of their physical abilities."[1]

The therapist asked me to do things like raise my legs,
squeeze her hand, and other activities. Then realizing that
my problem at that time was weakness in my leg, she gave
me a sheet with various exercises I could do in modera-
tion to strengthen those muscles. It was just an information session. Soon, "a determined spirit" was regularly
engaged in an exercise regime. I liked to exercise too!

Nurse Practitioner

Moving right along with my scheduled appointments, I
met with a nurse practitioner. I was not familiar with this

type of professional; I only knew of nurses. My first nurse practitioner's name was Margaret. Her function was to provide me with both clinical and educational services. We discussed the side effects of prednisone, constipation, salt intake, naps, and various other things. I began to find out how MS affected my bowels and regularity; constipation had become an area of concern to me. Little did I know that Margaret and I would have years of association.

MS Society

My doctor suggested that I contact the Multiple Sclerosis Society and familiarize myself with their services. In the days that followed, I did call the MS Society and even went to the local Washington office to learn where they were located and the services they offered. It was encouraging to know that this agency was in place to serve me and my family through education, counseling, and other areas of support.

Housekeeper

Spring 1986 was upon us. I noticed that the warmer weather was slowing my mobility, but I was still moving. It seemed I was fatigued all the time. With my responsibilities for Stacey, Ashley, a husband, a business, and having to take care of the house, I needed help! John and I discussed the issue of sending Stacey to preschool and hiring someone to help me take care of Ashley and do household chores. I welcomed the idea of sending Stacey to school and hiring a part-time housekeeper.

Stacey had just turned three and we thought it would be good for her to begin interacting with other children her age in a learning environment. I was teaching her how to count, recognize numbers, say her abc's, and to know her colors. I went to the teacher's supply store and bought posters she could point to and ask questions about. I put simple words up on her wall that she could pronounce and spell. We bought cassette tapes with songs, videos, books, puzzles, and other teaching aids. Stacey received a lot of attention from my mother and my sisters. Mom especially spoiled her. On weekends, my sister Becky, a kindergarten teacher, would sometimes take Stacey on field trips. During the summer months, they did all kinds of things together. I was thankful and so was Stacey!

We ran an ad in the newspaper for a part-time housekeeper and started checking out pre-schools. What a job! John and I prayed that both situations would be resolved quickly. By September, we had a wonderful housekeeper, and Stacey was registered in a church-sponsored preschool. Fortunately, Stacey didn't cry when we took her or cry to come home. She was ready for school and loved being there. It had a terrific playground where she got to burn off a lot of energy. What a blessing!

Susan, the housekeeper, was superb. She was so caring, loving, and dependable. She helped me keep the house clean and helped with ironing when time allowed. Susan didn't have to cook because I liked cooking and could handle that task. Her main responsibility was Ashley. However, Ashley gave her a fit. Ashley was a "mama's girl." It seemed that whenever I was not with her, she cried. She cried a lot because I would not just sit and hold her; I would give her to the housekeeper's charge.

Unlike Stacey, Ashley was not a baby to be calmed by a pacifier. (Once when we left Stacey's pacifier at home during a trip to New Jersey, Stacey, about a year old at the time, cried and kept saying "Nuk, Nuk" from the time we left home in Washington until John pulled into a mall we passed outside of Baltimore and purchased her a "Nuk.") Baby Ashley would have no parts of a Nuk or any other kind of pacifier. That little girl was something else! Nonetheless, the housekeeper was a good match for her spirited nature.

I thank God for bringing Susan into our lives. She was a ram in the bush during a period when I couldn't get to bed fast enough at the end of each day. With her help and John's, when the Christmas holiday season arrived, I was able to attend school programs, go shopping for toys, clothes, and other gifts, and help put up decorations. It was a wonderful time! Susan remained with us until she no longer could continue because of an asthma condition.

Chapter 11

First Baptist Church of Guilford

I thank my God upon every remembrance of you.
                                        Philippians 1:3

The new year 1987 came and it was time for more changes. We placed new items on the family agenda. Priority number one was a new church home. We decided to unite with my home church, First Baptist of Guilford in Columbia, Maryland—the church I grew up in, got saved in, got married in, and the church where my parents were long-time active members.

We transferred our membership from Canaan to Guilford in January. I have always believed in being an active member of a church, not one who just comes on Sunday and warms the pew. I wanted to be in the music ministry, so I joined the senior choir when I knew they needed members. Mom was the pianist and director for that choir. I loved singing with the senior choir because of the bond of love that radiated from its members. As a group, they encouraged and prayed for me, my husband, and my children during all of my MS battles. That meant a lot to me. But most of all, I have always loved singing to the glory of God. Besides, being a laborer for the Lord helped me keep my mind focused on Him and not my circumstances.

I functioned as a choir "helper" by sharing new music with Mom, teaching new songs to the choir, and helping to arrange medleys. Sometimes I was even able to stand and direct the choir. One Sunday Stacey, not yet four, helped me direct the choir. When Mom was not playing the piano, Stacey usually sat on the front pew with her. This particular Sunday I was directing the choir with Mom at the piano. Stacey got off the pew and stood behind me. Unbeknownst to me, when I raised my arms to direct, she raised hers as well, and she was doing what I was doing. I heard people in the congregation laughing, and when I looked back, I saw Stacey trying to direct like me. John had to come up and get her. She didn't like it and started calling, "Mommy, Mommy!" It was so cute. To this day I still have a special bond with that choir.

I appreciate how supportive the Guilford church family has always been to me, and to Mom and Dad in their various trials. When our entire family went through a crisis that involved Dad, I got to see another demonstration of the power of prayer and the need for "a determined spirit" during trying circumstances.

On October 21, 1987, my father, who was on the national board of the NAACP, went to Little Rock, Arkansas, for a board meeting. He wasn't feeling well when he left, but he went anyway. When he arrived at his hotel room, he laid on the bed and called down to the main desk to tell them that he was having chest pains. The ambulance came, and they had to force their way into his room. On the way to the hospital, he had a heart attack. Following an examination at the hospital, the doctors determined that bypass surgery was crucial. Mom was contacted, and she and Becky flew to Little Rock. Later that night, Dad had another heart attack and a stroke. Mom contacted us to let us know they had gotten there and give us Dad's status. The doctors felt he needed to be operated on without too much delay. Forty-eight hours later, Dad had triple bypass surgery. People all over the country were praying for Dad. Our pastor, Rev. Wright, flew to Little Rock. Dad wasn't out of the woods yet. Finally, my mother asked that all the children come to see him. My sister Kaye and I flew down together. We left on Thursday and returned on Sunday. I had never been there before, so I enjoyed the trip as much as I could. I was in remission and prayed that I would stay that way to better endure these circumstances.

When we got to Little Rock, we went straight to the hospital. Mom and Becky were there and were glad to see us! I was amazed at how bad Dad looked. I had made a tape of Stacey's greetings, and played it for him. When he tried to talk, it was a whisper, and it was hard to understand him. We visited him at the hospital as much as we could while we were there.

Sunday arrived and it was time for us to return home. A family in Little Rock had adopted my mom and sister and treated them like family. They had a big dinner for all of us before taking Kaye and me to the airport. The Halls were the kindest people. Kaye went to New Jersey and I came back to Washington.

Dad, Mom, and Becky were in Arkansas until November 27. Dad went directly from the hospital there to the hospital in Columbia, Maryland where they live. He stayed one month. Through Dad's experience, I gained further confirmation of the power of prayer. Thank God he is still with us as I write this account.

We remained members of First Baptist of Guilford until January 1990, when we transferred our membership to Parker Memorial Baptist Church in Silver Spring, Maryland. John and I had felt in our spirits that it was time to move on. This wasn't easy because Guilford was our home church. My parents were there, friends and church family were there, but it was time to go. We had to take our minds off the familiar surroundings and stay focused on God. We had to realize He was sending us somewhere else to grow and share; somewhere else to be laborers; somewhere else to be used by Him. Our season at Guilford was over, so in obedience we left.

Chapter 12

A Year to Remember—1987

To everything there is a season, a time for every purpose under heaven.

Ecclesiastes 3:1

The Need to Move

In six years of marriage our family had really grown. As 1987 began, a new year, the realization hit us that Somerset Place had become too small. We needed more space. Not only that, but the neighborhood was changing. Police activity seemed to have increased at the apartments located at the end of our street. We decided it would be better to be in a neighborhood with fewer apartments so near. And because Stacey would be going to first grade, we had to think about neighborhood schools for her. John prayed one day at dinner, "Lord, we thank You for the blessings You have bestowed upon us, but we need to move. Please help us!"

He began to busy himself with reading real estate ads, visiting neighborhoods, and researching school districts. We evaluated the options of an existing house versus a new house. We rode through neighborhoods that had decent schools the girls could attend. John was learning about the real estate market and facets involved in selling a home. He began to focus on the option of building a residence. We knew an architect who could design us one, but this involved finding a suitable lot. We wanted to remain in Washington where lots were scarce. In the areas where we desired to move, they were really scarce or out of our price range. We had several real estate agents working on our behalf. What an arduous task we had begun.

Bleeding Problem

I developed a prolonged bleeding problem during the latter months of 1986. I thought, *Lord, nothing else please. I do not want this problem for the length of time the woman with the flow of blood in the Bible had hers* (see Lk. 8:43). Dr. Sewell's diagnosis was that I had an ovarian cyst. I wanted to be certain, so I sought the opinion of another gynecologist. She concurred and wanted to treat me, but I returned to Dr. Sewell. "A determined spirit" helped me through this ordeal. I believed that my prolonged bleeding would be stopped. My gynecologist recommended trying hormone injections to try and shrink the cyst and stop the bleeding. If the injections did not solve the problem, I would have to undergo a D&C. The D&C took place on January 9, 1987. I prayed that it would be successful, and it was for a few years.

Almost a Year

It was March 31, 1987, when I returned to my neurologist's office. It had almost been a year. I had developed numbness in both hands and both feet. I had become more lethargic. However, my strength, reflexes, and sensory examinations were within normal limits. Even my walking was good. I was just having a mild MS exacerbation. I did not have to take prednisone, but I was given a prescription to fill if things worsened. I was advised to rest as much as possible, call if things did not get better, and "pray." I was both surprised and pleased to hear the neurologist acknowledge what I had already come to know—there is obviously value in seeking the face of the Lord.

Trip to the Bahamas

In May, my niece Kim graduated from college and was given a trip to the Bahamas. Mom, Stacey, Ashley, my friend Joyce, and I decided to accompany her. Stacey would be four years old in a month, and Ashley would be two years old in three months. This was their first out-of-the-country trip. Stacey was very excited, but Ashley didn't seem to be feeling so well. We probably should have stayed home, but we went anyway. I really wanted to go! Well, my intuition proved true with Ashley. After we had been flying about 30 minutes, she started throwing up and crying. She became cranky as a result. I had to comfort her as best I could. I just kept thinking, *She'll be better when we get there.*

When we finally got to the hotel, we ate and rested. We later went to the beach to catch some sun before dinner. At that time in my life, I could lie in the sun, get in the water, and run in the sand with no problems. When we reached the sand on the beach, Ashley would not walk. She didn't like the sand on her feet and had to be carried. (I could do that then too!) She was fine during the day, but in the evening her temperature rose and she began to vomit again. This pattern went on for the four days and three nights we were there. I felt so bad for her. She was miserable at night. Mom volunteered to attend to her one night so that I could get some relief. I was so grateful!

We finally made it back home and took Ashley to the doctor. We found out that she had pneumonia in her lungs. When I reflect back on this experience, I can't help but thank the Lord for sustaining her through His grace. Praise God, Ashley recovered!

Birthday Celebrations

Both Stacey's and Ashley's birthdays came with much celebrating. They always had a birthday party back then. On Stacey's first birthday, I had the balloon business and was able to do a balloon arch over her food and cake table. It was wonderful! I've always been blessed to be able to coordinate a gathering with no problem, and my husband, family, and friends are always there to help. I thank God for my husband, family, and the friends that He has placed in my life. I have never taken their love and support for granted. God is so good!

Ashley Goes to Day Care

John and I had a discussion about sending Ashley to day care at the school Stacey attended. We decided that in September she would go with Stacey. Well, Ashley was not as easy to part with as Stacey had been. On her first day, she cried and clung to us. She let us know from the start that she would only go two half-days a week. That was fine! She was only two, and if she desired not to go all day, every day, we understood. Ashley liked to be with me. She was a "mama's girl," and I could relate. I had been one too. John took the girls to school and I picked them up. It involved two trips for me. I picked Ashley up after lunch. We would both return home and take a nap. Then I would go back around 4:00 p.m. to pick up Stacey. I was able to do it, and loved doing it. This was one of the parental sacrifices that had to be made for my children. I learned to live with fatigue and believed with all my heart the Scripture, "I can do all things through Christ who strengthens me" (Phil. 4:13).

Closing Out the Year

December and the holidays were upon us once again. I had another CAT scan taken of my brain and paranasal sinuses. No abnormalities were seen and the test results were interpreted as normal. Praise God!

I attended my last worldly dance right before Christmas. The whole time I felt out of place, like I had no business there. The realization hit me, "I didn't." It was not an occasion where "a determined spirit" could glorify the Lord. I knew that was one stronghold I would surrender from that night on.

Chapter 13

The Trials of 1988

In everything give thanks; for this is the will of God in Christ Jesus for you.

1 Thessalonians 5:18

We were still looking at houses, old and new, as well as lots. By the end of 1987, God had given us a lot that we put a contract on and got. Hallelujah! A brand new home building project was about to begin. We were so thankful. We knew that we would be involved in our "new home" building project, but we didn't know what trials would beset us. I didn't know what MS difficulties I would experience, but I knew I had "a determined spirit" to carry me through whatever happened. And as it turned out, I had many doctor's visits that year.

New Year's 1988 was spent at our church watchnight service. I hadn't been in church on New Year's Eve for many, many years. John and I felt it was time to begin the year off right. In the Lord's house was the place to be. I am reminded of the Scripture in Romans 12:2, from *The Living Bible* that says:

Don't copy the behavior and customs of this world, but be a new and different person with a fresh newness in all you do and think. Then you will learn from your own experience how His ways will really satisfy you.

So from that New Year's Eve forward, we have spent our new years in worship with God, praising and thanking Him for all He's done and will yet do in our life.

Trial #1, Optic Neuritis Strikes

I came out of remission with optic neuritis, so my first appointment that year was the ophthalmologist. On March 7, I went to his office with pain, blurriness, and little sight in my right eye. I underwent a lot of visual tests that day. My vision measured 20/40. It was determined that I would be given a course of prednisone. I was prescribed 20mg tablets to take three times a day for ten days. I wasn't as salt conscious then as I am today, so I gained weight during the treatment period. My face became round and my normally slim legs got fat. When I went to see the ophthalmologist at the end of the ten days, the optic neuritis was as prevalent on March 17 as it had been on March 7. I was to continue the prednisone dosage for three more days and then begin to take less per day. I was given a taper-down schedule to follow. Yes, I was tired of not seeing 20/20, but I believed that my eyesight would return to 20/20. On April 19, I had a return appointment. My eyesight was 20/30 with all indications that 20/20 was coming. In prior visits the color red was dull and dim, but that day it was bright. I was elated! To top it off, I didn't have to return for six months. I thanked God every step of the way.

Trial #2, Broken Ankle Experiences

It was a beautiful day! I had a date to have lunch with my friend Gloria. The following account was recorded from memory, as well as from my diary notes for Thursday, May 26, 1988.

My first stop was at John's place of employment where I kissed and dropped him off. My next stop was the downtown location of the Volunteer Clearinghouse. My purpose for going there was to see what opportunities were available in counseling in the DC area. I felt that there might be something I could volunteer for, even having MS. I then proceeded to the Church Music Store located uptown. I wanted to purchase a hymn book and sheet music that my mother could use with the senior choir. It was a very worthwhile stop. I left the music store at 12:35 p.m. I was to meet Gloria at 1:00 p.m. I was excited because it had been a good morning and I was having lunch with a friend!

I drove from downtown Washington up to midtown. I arrived at Gloria's office at 12:55 p.m., and we walked to a restaurant two blocks away. Unfortunately, it had a long line, so we went to another one. As we entered the restaurant, I noticed that the steps we climbed were in need of repair. Once inside I thought no more about the steps. We both enjoyed a California steak sandwich, which is like a London Broil with onions and mushrooms on top of toast. For our beverage, we drank iced tea. Lunch was filling, especially with the french fries. We both enjoyed the meal and the fellowship.

We got up to leave the restaurant around 2:00 p.m. Gloria went down the steps ahead of me. I stepped down the first two steps, but when I stepped on the third step, my foot slipped and I fell down the remaining steps and ended up on my behind on the bottom step. My leg was twisted behind me. I felt a sharp shock of pain up my leg to my knee. I just knew my leg was broken. I sat there, wincing and ooing. Gloria turned around and said, "Oh my God!" The owner had been at the door when we exited the restaurant, and she came down the steps and said, "Are you all right? Can you straighten your leg?" For a while I couldn't do anything except sit there and hurt. When the owner asked if I could straighten my leg, I couldn't even feel it. I told her that I had multiple sclerosis. The injury was on the right leg, and my right side is usually the numbest and the weakest. As the initial numbness started to subside, I could feel severe pain in my leg. She instructed some waitresses to get some ice, a glass of water, and to call an ambulance. The last thing I wanted was a glass of water.

I wanted my husband. I told Gloria to go call him. I also told her that I had better go have my leg X-rayed. While she was gone I examined my foot. It had a laceration on top, which was bleeding, and it was swelling fast. I tried to pick up my leg with my hands and saw that my right foot was dangling. The owner put the towel of ice on my foot, as we waited for the ambulance. Gloria returned and said that John's office was trying to track him down. He was at a meeting on Capitol Hill. The ambulance arrived in six minutes, and the driver looked at my ankle and said that it might be broken. I was praying hard and asking God to give me strength to endure all that I was about to go through. I was also telling myself to be strong and no tears. I knew that if I cried, I would fall apart. No tears were shed and I endured.

I was loaded into the ambulance. Gloria came out and told me she had to hang up with John's office because she had been put on hold. She would call them back from the hospital. I was taken to George Washington University Hospital. I left Gloria at the telephones and was wheeled into a room in Emergency. A nurse came in, as did a physician who stated that the ankle looked like it was broken. The nurse cut my pantyhose off the right foot and applied ice packs. The physician came in and said that X-rays would be taken as soon as the X-ray room was free. Thank God I was alert and cooperative. The nurse asked when I had received my last tetanus shot. I told her a long time ago, so she immediately gave me one. Next the nurse was told to call the IV therapy people to hook me up.

IV therapy arrived. The first person who tried to put in the IV kept messing up. I was praying big time! Finally, the second person got it in. The IV was inserted in my left arm and I received sugar water, better known as glucose. Five vials of blood were taken as well. While awaiting X-rays, a surgeon came in. He observed and evaluated my ankle, asked me to wiggle my toes and took the pulse in my foot. He then stated that the ankle looked broken.

Gloria was allowed to come in. She relayed to me that John's office had tracked him down and he was on his way. I said, "Thank You, Jesus!" Gloria couldn't believe that I hadn't shed a tear. I told her that I was praying for strength. I was given a gown to change into in the meantime. John finally arrived and I felt so relieved. I cried when I saw him, and he just hugged and hugged me, and assured me that it was going to be all right.

They soon wheeled me into X-ray. I had to turn my foot various ways. It hurt! I was taken out of X-ray and pushed into a hall space until the X-rays were developed. I told Gloria that I had to go to the bathroom. She told the resident surgeon, and I was wheeled into a room where a nurse gave me a bedpan. Afterward, the doctors returned with the X-rays. John and Gloria returned as well. I had broken my ankle in three places. The doctor pointed out the breaks and said that they would set the ankle in a cast.

John and Gloria decided that she would go pick up Stacey and Ashley. When she left, the nurse put something in my IV, and the doctors began the process of putting the cast on. When the cast was completed, I was wheeled back out in the hall. I remained there until a room was available for me. Finally, at 6:15 p.m., I was admitted to the hospital and was given a room with a roommate. A surgeon was scheduled to visit the next day to discuss prognosis, options, length of time for the hospital stay, etc. But one thing was certain, I would be staying at George Washington University Hospital this night.

John made calls to check on the girls. He had contacted Mom and Dad while I was in the Emergency Room. They were to come to the house after Mom's choir rehearsal. I was brought a tray of food, which John and I both ate. I buzzed the nurse and asked for pain pills, but they didn't work very well. I was hurting! John left the hospital around 8:00 p.m. so he could go pick up my car from the public garage. When he got home, he called me, and I spoke to Stacey and Ashley. They wanted me to come home right then. I assured them that I would be home soon. I also talked to Mom and Dad who were there at my house. I called my sister Becky next. The girls were to go with her on Friday to the school where she taught. She was doing a circus with her kindergarten class. I told her that I would send my video camera along so she could have her husband video the performance for me.

After the various telephone conversations, I lay on my bed resting. Then the resident surgeon came by to see how I was doing and to make sure my foot was elevated. He said that surgery was tentatively being scheduled for 12:30 p.m. on the next day. After midnight, I wouldn't be able to eat or drink anything. I was given the name of the surgeon who would review my X-rays and discuss the options with John and me. I asked for a pain injection after the resident surgeon left.

I was beginning to settle down when my roommate began a tirade of crying, cursing, and buzzing for the nurse. This went on from 10:00 p.m. until 4:00 a.m. What a night! I didn't get much sleep at all, especially while having to keep my leg elevated and straight. It was a real drag! The next morning the nurses kept saying, "You are charted for surgery at 12:30 so you can't have anything to eat." I focused my mind on things besides food and ignored my stomach growling. John arrived around 11:00 a.m. At 12:30 p.m. the television lady came and turned the paid TV service on. John had contacted them when he came in that morning. He also called the surgeon's office around 1:00 p.m. to find out what was causing the delay. We were informed that he would be by after his last office appointments around 3:30 p.m. He also communicated that I could receive meals. If surgery was going to be done, it wouldn't be until the following Wednesday. Hallelujah!

John and I shared lunch. I watched television and napped. Finally, around 5:00 p.m. the surgeon stopped in and said, "I'm on my way to see the X-rays, I'll be right back." When he returned he sat down and explained the pros and cons of having surgery. He talked technical jargon. To make a long story short, surgery would guarantee a proper fit using pins or screws. After surgery, I would have a shorter cast (to the knee) and the wearing time would be 6-8 weeks versus 10-12 weeks with a long cast (to the hip). I would gain more mobility. He told John and me to think it over. We were to contact his office with our decision. He told me I could go home Friday evening or Saturday. However, I could not be discharged until someone gave me lessons on using crutches. Then the surgeon left, but I must say his bedside manner was nothing to brag about.

While contemplating the surgical options, I cried a lot. I didn't want to undergo surgery and more pain! I thank God for my husband and the Holy Spirit. I was given insight and wisdom as to why I must choose the option of surgery. I had children, ages five and three, I had a husband, and I had MS. I got myself together emotionally. I needed to accept the scenario that provided best for my mobility. I opted to go for surgery and the shorter cast.

A dinner tray was brought in, and I rested for a while. A man from Physical Therapy was sent to teach me how to use the crutches. He brought me proper foot attire and another gown to use as a bathrobe. I prayed for God to help me. This was the first time I had gotten up since the whole ordeal began, so my leg felt really heavy when it was let down off the bed. Learning to walk with those crutches made me realize that we take so much for granted—things like walking, talking, etc. God showers so many blessings on us that we just need to thank Him more. Even though what I was going through was unpleasant, I just pictured in my mind the cross and Jesus hanging on it just for me. God is so good, and I love Him so much!

I walked down halls and up and down three steps. I was exhausted! We went back to the room and John helped me walk to the bathroom. Finally, I got back into bed. John left at 9:15 p.m. I prayed and rested. I was learning that no matter what circumstance I would face, I had to trust God. I had to hold onto His Word! John 14:27 says, "Peace I leave with you, My peace I give to you.... Let not your heart be troubled, neither let it be afraid." I believed His promise and knew He was right with me. He had brought me through the ankle ordeal so far, and I knew He wasn't going to leave me now. It was a good sleeping night! Saturday morning I awakened knowing my decision was to have the surgery. The surgeon's office was contacted.

A Few Days at Home

I was going home for a spell. Thank You, God! I could leave anytime after 10:00 a.m. And I was thinking, *Hurry up, John, I'm ready to get out of here!* I was being discharged with re-admittance scheduled for three days later. The date would be June 1, and I would have surgery that day. I was going home with a pair of crutches and Tylenol #3 for pain.

John arrived, and I was wheeled to the patient's exit. He had Mom and Dad's car so I could sit in the back with my leg stretched out on the seat. John helped me in, and we went home. Not being adept with the crutches yet, I had to master getting up our three frontyard steps. I'm glad my balance, strength, and coordination were on it that day, otherwise John would have had to carry me. It was so hard! Thank God "a determined spirit" was present and accounted for. The long-legged plaster cast was heavy and yielded no flexibility. It was very hot outside.

We finally made it to the front door! Mom and Dad were there to greet us. Stacey and Ashley were playing on the deck in the backyard. John settled me in on the sofa in the living room and then left to go fill prescriptions. The girls ran in to see me and showered me with hugs and kisses. Ashley was hesitant with her first approach but soon overcame that. Stacey had lots of questions. They really had missed me and vice versa. I was so happy to be home with my family. Both girls would become really upset if I tried to get up and retrieve something. I had to keep my leg elevated because of the swelling. I felt like my cast was on too tight, but I didn't know. I had no experience in wearing one before. However I was about to find out what was going on underneath that cast; why my toes hurt so much and why there was such pain in the area below my baby toe. Soon, very soon I would know.

Casts

The three days rolled around very fast, and I was back in the hospital. Upon removal of the cast, the surgeon found that I had a large pressure sore. It was on the upper right bottom and side of my foot, below my last three toes.

He was very concerned because it was near a gangrene condition, and wondered why I hadn't come to see him in his office. I told him, "I felt my toes hurting, but I thought they were supposed to. I didn't know. I've never worn a cast before." He said that I would probably lose that skin and tissue area, which I eventually did. During subsequent weeks, that particular area was affected by every cast I had put on after the surgery.

During the surgery, three metal screws were put in my ankle. Two on one side and one on the other. They would be there permanently. I knew that I would never consider having them removed. This was it! The surgery went well and I was discharged from the hospital on June 3, 1988.

Despite the cast and being less mobile than I desired, I still met my life's demands as best I could. We celebrated Stacey's birthday at her school. There I was, cast and all, sitting in the midst of her party. Games, cake, and dancing by the children made for an enjoyable birthday celebration. Stacey had her fifth birthday on June 9 and graduated from pre-kindergarten on June 15. My oldest baby was growing up. I was glad, but saddened sometimes when I realized that she wasn't a baby anymore. She was going to be in kindergarten in September. My how time had flown!

I wore a cast for two months. It was changed several times because of the extreme discomfort I was experiencing. I was prescribed pain medication and four weeks of antibiotics. During one of the initial office visits after the surgery, it appeared my ankle was determined to have an infection. I had to keep my leg elevated the entire two months. As a result, I was physically carried up and down stairs and assisted with personal hygiene and dressing. I was unable to significantly help care for my young daughters. John stayed home with me for four weeks. With the help of "a determined spirit," family, and friends, we made it.

On June 30, 1988, still on my crutches, I visited my neurologist. Numerous incidents had occurred since my last visit with him, including two episodes of MS. His examination revealed no sensory loss in my upper extremities, and I did well on the strength and coordination tests. Thank God.

Physical Therapy

The day finally arrived when the plaster cast was done away with. I could now wear an air cast. This was the go-ahead to begin physical therapy, which I started on August 4 at a diagnostic center. My therapist did his job well and worked me hard! The therapy was designed to reduce the extensive swelling and to restore mobility and flexibility in my ankle.

Someone would drive me to therapy. We would park, go inside the building, and take the elevator to the correct floor. I started with therapy twice a week, then went to once a week. All kinds of exercises were done to and for my ankle. This center even had computerized exercise equipment that talked to you. It was definitely advanced state of the art.

Parking at the center became a hassle, since I didn't have handicapped tags at that time. I subsequently sought and found a new therapist who was more accessible. The latter situation worked out well, since I was still having office visits with the surgeon. I eventually got to a point where I could drive myself, using my left leg.

It was at this time that John bought me an exercise bicycle. I made the request known, and he honored it. I don't ask him for much, but there haven't been many things in my life that I asked him for that he didn't get. He's a wonderful husband, and I love him so much. The bike had been recommended earlier by a physical therapist I had consulted in May 1986. Now definitely was the time for its use. I rode it every other day, with the aim of strengthening my legs and ankles. I worked hard on the bicycle, and it became a regular part of my daily routine. Even my neurologist has been pleased with my use of the exercise bicycle because of its positive effect on my overall conditioning.

I believed that the day would come when I would have no pain in my ankle. For a time I could always tell when it was going to rain; my ankle would ache so badly. In cold weather and dampness, the ache would manifest itself again. But praise God, today I am healed of the ankle agony. I still don't have full flexibility in the ankle, but my bones are healed. Hallelujah!

August 14 was Ashley's birthday. I wasn't about to let her day go by without a celebration. The physical therapy was helping my mobility, so we decided to give her a spaghetti dinner party. It went over well, and with God's help, "a determined spirit" was able to see it through.

Chapter 14

The Moving Plan Materialized

Behold, I will do a new thing, now it shall spring forth;
shall you not know it?

Isaiah 43:19a

My focus was on the February 1989 move to our newly-built house. There were boxes to be packed and furniture to be purchased, including that baby grand piano I had promised myself. There were appliances to choose, carpet and wallpaper to pick out, things to give or throw away, etc. Moving brings its own anticipation. I thank God He was there to guide us. I thank Him for the strength and perseverance He gave to me. My days were full and busy. I didn't faithfully rest everyday, but I did so when I could. Fatigue tried to get the best of me, but I kept on moving with "a determined spirit."

September arrived, and it was "return to school" time. Somehow we managed to do school shopping. Stacey was excited about going to kindergarten at the neighborhood public school. I took her to school at 9:00 a.m. and picked her up at 3:00 p.m. John took Ashley to the day care center on his way to work, and I picked her up by 12:30 p.m. The routine soon got underway, and we began moving right along.

I realized that even though we were preparing to move, my multiple sclerosis hadn't gone anywhere. On October 28, 1988, I saw my neurologist. Unfortunately, I was having an exacerbation. I was numb on my entire right side and had been having numbness in both legs. Upon examination, this is what the neurologist documented: "She had decreased pin sensation over the entire right face, arm, and leg. She also has decreased coordination in the left leg on heel-to-shin. Gait is stiff-legged and she has difficulty with tandem gait." In testing gait, the doctor watched me walk. *Tandem gait* is walking a straight heel-to-toe line. I was having problems with both constipation and fatigue. I was scheduled to talk with the nurse practitioner about the constipation. We did talk, and that's when prunes became a big part of my diet. I liked prunes so I had no problem eating them or drinking the juice. They are a good snack—just be near the bathroom!

The neurologist put me on the prednisone taper-down course. If my fatigue persisted, there were other drug options I could try. When I left his office, I had the "here we go again" attitude. Prednisone did work well for me then. I was to contact him when the course was completed. My prayer was, "God, please sustain me to meet my life's demands. Please give me a remission."

We made it through Thanksgiving and the holidays. Christmas was happy because God was blessing us, but sad because it was our last Christmas in the house on Somerset Place. Packing and planning to move was the order of the day.

Moving Day

Moving day finally arrived, February 20, 1989. The sun shone brightly. It was a little bit cool, but a great day for moving. We rented a large U-Haul truck to carry our belongings. Use of this truck resulted in the need for only one major trip to the new residence, which was only five minutes away. Our vehicles were used to make return trips to pick up plants, and other things. From the time the first piece of furniture was carried out, I operated the video camera to capture it all. Boy, am I glad I did!

The day began early. The truck was loaded as tightly as possible by our moving crew, which consisted of family and friends (Thanks Sonny!). Stacey and Ashley were allowed to stay home from school and were very active. They were excited and curious. At one point early on Stacey said, "Mom, I'm thirsty." My response very directly stated was, "Go downstairs, get a Sssip It (a straw drink), and drink it!" I also told her to give one to her sister. It was one time among many that I knew I had to take a deep breath and remain calm. I knew I had to listen to the Holy Spirit telling me to let the fruit mature (I refer to the fruit of love, joy, peace, patience, kindness, gentleness, faithfulness, and self-control). But it was hard, especially when I thought about the work to be done at the other end of the move.

The truck was finally loaded up and moved out. This was the culmination of many dreams, many challenges, and many prayers. The project had required much patience and perseverance. You just don't know! The Lord had sustained us, and I was so thankful.

Our New Residence

The real work was yet to come, for the new residence was on a hill and there were 25 steps to be climbed just to enter the front door. Some things could be taken through the backdoors or the garage, but not many. There were three floors, so there were several sets of steps that had to be traversed.

The master bedroom was the only thing on the top floor. The master bedroom bath had a jacuzzi bath and a large adjoining stall shower. We had skylights in the room, a fireplace, ceiling fan, and a little balcony outside. It was quite nice! When we moved in, all the inside work had not yet been completed—like the railings, bookcases, and trim work. So when we went to the master bedroom, it was a nervous ascension due to the fact that the railing wasn't in place yet. But I got used to it. Stacey's and Ashley's rooms were on the first floor, along with the guest bedroom. The family room, kitchen, breakfast area, and dining room were on the first floor as well. There was a step down from the hallway to the entrance foyer, off of which was the living room and library. The piano and our extensive collection of books went into the library. You could sit on the steps that led to the master bedroom and see the library through an opening. This was an exceptionally nice feature of the house, especially when someone was playing the piano.

The last set of steps led to the ground floor where another family room, the girls' playroom, my office, the laundry room, and another bedroom were found. It was a large contemporary house, with loads of windows and high ceilings. It had plenty of closet and storage space.

We had furniture deliveries all day. There was furniture for the dining room, living room, family room, and master bedroom. Another piece of furniture to be delivered was our new baby grand piano. It merits special attention because I had always wanted a piano. Climbing 25 steps with a piano was an effort worth video taping. We did just that! It arrived at 1:00 p.m. To God be the glory, for three men got that piano inside and in place by 1:32 p.m. I was ecstatic. Yeah! Stacey and Ashley could begin lessons. The possibility existed now that even I could take them, continuing where I had left off 20 years ago. John had no interest in learning to play himself. Mom, the pianist, could now play when she came to visit. It was such a blessing to receive this as well as the other deliveries. Thank you Lord.

My mom and Becky were there through all of the moving process. My sister Virginia arrived after we had gotten everything unloaded and the piano was in place. She came with a cake, which was right on time. Another pair of hands. Thank God! The major moving task had been completed.

We began to settle into our new residence. As a result of the break-in at the prior residence, John and I vowed we would have a security system in this home. Being a number one priority, it was installed before we moved in. While becoming acclimated to the new system and its various features, we regularly tripped the alarm. This resulted in impromptu visits by different policemen in our district. We finally got it together, became familiar with the system, and it worked!

Priority number two was to have the railings and bookcases built. A month after we had moved in, we contracted the work to a carpenter. The day he came and began his work, was the day I had my first flat-on-my-face fall. He had laid his canvas on the front hall at the library door. I was going to play the piano and my right foot dragged when I went to step on the canvas, causing me to fall flat on my face. It hurt, and I cried. I picked myself up and prayed to God for it to be manageable. In the bathroom, I discovered a cut below my lower lip that was bleeding badly and beginning to swell. The carpenter had stepped out during this time to go purchase some materials, and I was kind of glad. I was embarrassed that I had fallen. I went to the kitchen and got ice to make an ice pack, then I called John in tears. After I talked to him, I called my mother. Talking to both of them calmed my nerves, and I was able to rest until the carpenter returned. When he returned I told him what had happened. When he asked if there was anything he could do, I thanked him for asking but said, "No." He apologized for the canvas being on the floor, but I told him it wasn't his fault. To this day, I only retain a small scar, and my mouth is not out of sync. Thank You, God! That fall helped prepare me for future falls that have occurred due to my leg dragging at times. It was right after the fall that God started speaking to me from Second Corinthians 12:8-10, a passage that deals with the apostle Paul and the thorn in his flesh he asked God to remove three times. This was the beginning of "the thorn in the flesh" message that has been communicated to me, time and again from God.

The day eventually arrived when the inside work was completed and we had nothing else to unpack. We began to enjoy our new residence. I realized that another season of experiences was beginning.

Chapter 15

Out of Remission Again

*Rejoicing in hope, patient in tribulation, continuing
steadfastly in prayer.*

Romans 12:12

During the spring of 1989 I was really fatigued from
the previous months of moving and unpacking. I was out
of remission and foreseeing a visit to my neurologist.
Nonetheless, I held to the goal of taking some college
classes in the fall, praying I would be able to do so.

On April 28 I had an appointment with my neurologist. I was having an exacerbation resulting in a numbness
on my left side that had been occurring for six weeks. I
also had numbness on the right side from the knee down.
It had always amazed me how my feet could be numb yet
I could still walk while barely being able to feel them. Various tests were given to measure sensation and vibration in
my legs, which disclosed markedly impaired responses. I
was experiencing optic neuritis as well. Dr. Edelson noted
that my attitude was excellent, in spite of the circumstances. I felt "a determined spirit" showing forth again.
The pros and cons of a short course of prednisone were

discussed, and it was decided to put me on one. One of my concerns that day was the fatigue I was feeling. I started running out of energy by noon each day—every day! He discussed some possible drugs I could take for this problem. My mind-set was "No more drugs." Prednisone was enough, especially when there could be side effects. No way! I would exercise faith, and stand on God's Word that by His stripes I am healed.

I had my follow-up visit with Dr. Edelson on June 12. I felt better when I was taking the prednisone; it always gave me lots of energy. But upon stopping the prescribed course, I went back to feeling the way I had initially. I still had decreased sensation in my lower extremities. Fatigue was still a major problem. I was given a prescription drug to try. I never did have the prescription filled. It stayed in my drawer.

I went to the ophthalmologist on July 5. I was having double vision. I had never experienced this before. I knew that this could occur with MS patients, but it had passed me by until now. I had just finished a course of steroids not terribly long before, so I had to play the waiting game. When the vision wanted to focus itself, it would. I had to believe that. My vision did return to normal, so I cancelled my July 24 appointment. I saw no need to go because things were back on track. Praise God!

By fall of 1989 I was pursuing the goal I set forth in the spring. I enrolled as a college student and was taking two classes. "A determined spirit" forged ahead once again. Even though I had multiple sclerosis, there was nothing wrong with my mind, so I registered for Accounting I and Computer Applications. I had a computer and wanted to be able to use the various software that had just been installed. The course included WordPerfect, D-base III and Lotus. I had some learning to do. Little did I know that by the end of the school year, I would have another testimony about perseverance. I didn't even focus on walking as a difficulty for me. My mind was set on fulfilling my various roles as a wife, mother, and student.

It was interesting to be a student again. It wasn't easy, but I believed what the Scriptures told me in Philippians 4:13, that I could "do all things through Christ who strengthens me." "A determined spirit" clung to this Scripture, accepted it as a challenge, and brought it to fruition by semester's end. I attended classes during the daytime when the girls were in school. Stacey was in first grade, and Ashley was in pre-kindergarten. I did most of my studying when I had no classes or other commitments and at night when the girls were asleep.

Due to the ankle injury, I still didn't have the flexibility in my ankle that I would have liked to. Stepping up and down on sidewalks was hard, but I could still manage. I thanked God for the elevator at the college because my Accounting class was on the second floor. I only used steps when I absolutely had to. I made it through the first semester with straight A's. This encouraged me to take another semester of classes.

On November 20, 1989, I returned to Dr. Edelson's office. Three days prior to this appointment I had another onset of optic neuritis. I was experiencing pain and loss of vision in the right eye. Dr. Edelson wanted me to try a steroid treatment of Solu-Medrol. This drug was to be administered three consecutive days by IV in the doctor's office.

Then I would take prednisone on a taper-down course for 15 days. This treatment was designed to hopefully reverse the exacerbation process and kick in faster than just taking prednisone in pill form. I didn't mind the IV because I have excellent veins. The treatment time took one hour.

At this point I would like to highlight the goals of drug therapy of any disease with a quote:

> "The goals of therapy of any disease are to prevent the initial occurrence (prophylactic treatment), to arrest the progress of the disease and prevent future attacks (curative treatment), to repair the damaged tissues and restore them to normal function (restorative treatment), to treat symptoms, to prevent and relieve complications (symptomatic treatment), and to help the patient to adjust to the disability and achieve as much function as possible with the remaining normal tissues or parts (rehabilitative therapy)."[1]

As drug therapy related to me, symptomatic treatment was used. Many of my "primary symptoms" such as weakness, spasticity, incoordination, numbness, and blurred vision would clear partially or completely after a Solu-Medrol treatment.

I returned to the ophthalmologist again on December 26, 1989. My eyes were twitching badly. They were examined and my vision was measured. I had just finished a course of steroids, so I kept the faith with the Scripture, "Wait on the Lord, be of good courage" (Ps. 27:14a).

We had celebrated our first Christmas in our home on Kalmia. It was a blessed time, yet I was feeling low because of the many MS exacerbations I'd experienced that year. My friend Pat knew what I had been going through and asked if she could have her friend Theresa intercede on my behalf. I told her, "Please do." Right after Christmas she called and asked me if they could come over to pray and share Scriptures with me. I told her, "Yes," and they came on Saturday. Theresa is a God-fearing woman who is well-learned in the Scriptures. She clearly demonstrates her love for the Father. She shared *many* Scriptures with me regarding sickness and healing. Both she and Pat prayed with me. I didn't even own a study Bible! I used John's Bible that day. I was so embarrassed when it came to locating particular verses in the Bible. The Bible I owned was the one I had been given as a child by my mom. Boy, did I have work to do! I needed to learn the books of the Bible, and become proficient in locating them when needed. Their visit helped instill in me a deep hunger to study and learn God's Word. I just thank God for the blessings received that day and for bringing another strong Spirit-filled saint into my life. When they left, my spirit had been lifted and revived. There would be further fellowship with them in the future.

Chapter 16

A New Church Home

For the word of God is living and powerful, and sharper than any two-edged sword.

Hebrews 4:12a

By the end of 1989, both John and I knew it was time to pray for a new church home. We were both hungry for the Word, and we wanted to grow through Bible study. On Sundays we were traveling quite a distance to church in Columbia, Maryland. I also went there every Tuesday evening for my choir rehearsal, and on Saturdays for choir rehearsal for Stacey and Ashley. If it was God's will, we really wanted a church closer to home.

The search for a new church home did not stop my MS symptoms. On January 5, 1990, I had a visit with Dr. Edelson. I was having an exacerbation with much gait difficulty. I had to do various gait tests, which included walking heel-to-toe, walking regular, walking on my toes, and walking on my heels. By observing my standing and walking, the doctor could tell if I was having sensory loss, weakness, spasticity, or difficulty in walking caused by a loss of balance or incoordination of the legs known as ataxia. Although I had just finished a steroid course only two-and-one-half weeks earlier for optic neuritis, I was placed on prednisone again. The doctor said that if it didn't result in a full recovery, I would be given a Solu-Medrol treatment.

A few weeks later, I returned to school. The prednisone was not working, and I was dragging. On the first day of classes, my legs refused to cooperate. I parked my van and was walking from the parking lot to my class. My legs just stopped, and I had trouble moving them. It was as if the message "walk" was being short-circuited at the message center in my brain. I didn't know whether I would get from point A to point B. It was nerve-racking! I prayed and asked God to please help me make it to my class, promising that when I got home I would call my neurologist to receive the Solu-Medrol treatment. He answered my prayer, and I was able to lift my legs. However, they felt like I was carrying a 50-pound weight on each one. The right leg felt heavier than the left. "A determined spirit" stepped in and reminded me that I was going to make it through this semester. I prayed that the Solu-Medrol would work positively for me. I realized that gait disorder was now manifesting.

"Gait disorders varying from an inability to walk the usual distance to an inability to walk at all are the principal problems of patients with MS. This may be a result of any combination of the aforementioned: weakness, spasticity, or ataxia combined with easy fatigability."[1]

I called the neurologist when I got home and relayed to him how the prednisone had not worked, what was going on with my legs, and that I needed the Solu-Medrol treatment. He consented, and I was scheduled for three consecutive days of treatment.

Church Search

Determined to begin the new year right, on the second Sunday in January 1990, I retrieved the telephone directory and began calling some nearby churches. The first church I called did not answer. The second church had an answering machine. My third call was to Parker Memorial, a church we had passed many Sundays on our way to Columbia. A pleasant man answered. I asked what time their services were held, and he said 8:00 a.m. and 11:00 a.m. He went on to say, "service is going on right now, why don't you come on over." So we went there. The church was pretty full, and the service moved right along. There was a warm welcome extended to visitors. The senior pastor was a young man, about 28 years old. He had just been selected for pastorship in December. I don't remember the title of the sermon he preached that Sunday, but he certainly dissected the Word of God. I noticed that the members carried and used their Bibles during the service. I loved it! I later came to understand why this church was a Bible preaching, Bible teaching one, and why the pastor had a reputation for being an expository preacher.

The Bible study class was held on Thursday nights, so I decided to go that Thursday. I was amazed at the attendance on a Thursday evening! I knew something powerful was being taught to motivate people to be there on a Thursday night. I was excited when I got home and told John what I had observed.

We returned the next Sunday for the 11:00 a.m. service. The choir, which I was later to join, was wonderful. On Thursday evening I asked my niece Deidre to keep Stacey and Ashley until I found out if they had a nursery, and John and I went to the Bible study. We both enjoyed being taught from the Word of God. This preacher was an excellent teacher. On the way home, we discussed the possibility of uniting with this church. We prayed and asked the Lord what we were to do.

We continued to visit through the month of January. I met with the pastor and asked some pertinent questions. He gave me a copy of his doctrinal position and stated that he exercised an open-door policy when someone needed to talk to him. I told him that we were considering uniting with this church. When I left his office, I felt that he was God-directed and not self-directed. He was very articulate, easy to talk with, friendly, and had a humble spirit. A new pastorship was certainly a gift from God. I didn't want to feel or see arrogance, but humility and thankfulness. My spirit sensed the latter qualities, and I was glad I met with him.

I once heard a sermon that listed three things to desire when searching for a new church home: a pastor that has a vision, looks for lost souls, and is mission minded. This sermon was playing in my mind as I met with the pastor. I knew that I needed to be fed spiritually, so that was my number one priority. By hearing him preach more than once, I knew this preacher could feed me well from the Word of God. We looked forward to learning from him.

I saw Dr. Edelson on January 19 and relayed to him that I felt like the Solu-Medrol had not worked as well this last time. Usually, it would kick in after the third treatment, and I would be raring to go—but not this time. My legs felt heavy and stiff (spastic paraparesis). The doctor noted that my gait was wide-based and stiff. I could not rise from a low stool without using my arms. At that time he thought I probably was going into a phase of chronic progressive MS. This means that you will have less or no remissions over a course of time, which indicates the MS is progressing. "A determined spirit" kept me pressing on no matter what.

The first Sunday in February, John and I united with Parker Memorial based on Christian experience. I looked forward to growing in the Word and having a church family. We went through New Members Class and received the right hand of fellowship. By the time I finished this class, the church family knew I had multiple sclerosis. Ascending and descending steps, which this church had, was a difficulty for me, as was walking to the pew to sit down. Nevertheless, I always had help other than John if I needed it. That was a blessing. Hallelujah. We had found a new church home!

By June 12, 1990, I was back in Dr. Edelson's office again. My vision was acting up, my left eye headed toward optic neuritis. I could tell because the light in the left eye was getting dark, I could only read large print with the eye, and the color red was decreased. In addition, my gait was abnormal and walking was difficult. I was asked to do various gait tests, one being the tandem (toe-to-heel) test. The tandem test was hard to do, as were the others; so I didn't perform well. Once again I needed Solu-Medrol treatment. I prayed, "Lord, please let it work, please help my legs function to the perfection for which You created them to function."

I visited my neurologist again on August 20, 1990, following our family vacation to the Bahamas. Praise God! The treatment of Solu-Medrol significantly improved my vision and my walking. I only had minimal blurring of vision in both eyes and a feeling of tightness in my right leg. Dr. Edelson noted that I was *not* walking with a cane, even though I was still having some gait difficulty. His summary was as follows: "Her general well-being is much improved. Thus she seems to be in remission and hopefully will stay there." The visit was a good one. When I left his office, I stopped at the pharmacy in the building and purchased a cane. I decided that the cane could help me keep my balance when walking, since my right foot was dragging sometimes and there was weakness in my right leg. I had to learn how to walk with the cane and become comfortable using it.

The following is an entry from my journal, written December 4, 1990:

I came out of remission, one week ago today. I noticed my legs were real heavy to move—it was like lifting steel—and were extremely numb. I kept trudging. By Wednesday, I was dragging my left leg and had to pull out my cane. I was numb from the waist down and my hands were getting real numb and stiff. I had jury duty on Monday, which required a lot of sitting, and several times I needed to walk up an escalator that wasn't working. By the time I got home, I was wiped out. Such activity contributed to my "out of remission" status. Wednesday night I had choir rehearsal, but John wouldn't let me go. He insisted that I stay in the bed. What a gem of a husband I have; it was the best advice. Thursday I called the Neurology Center.

I returned to Dr. Edelson's office on December 7, 1990. I was having another exacerbation. I had numbness from the waist down on the right side, and had developed increasing weakness of my right leg and right hand. I *was* walking with my cane.

Walking now required the use of the cane as an aid. The more exacerbations I had, the weaker my legs became. I did not become discouraged or embarrassed by it. I was just so thankful to be able to *walk*, no matter what I had to use to do so. "A determined spirit" helped me when walking was good or bad. I realized that I was not able to walk long distances any more, but I could still walk. I knew that motor impairment would probably become a problem for me because of the weakness and spasticity I had in my legs. Walking had become difficult because there had been losses in my strength, muscle tone, and balance. My foot muscles had become weak in the right foot, resulting in the foot dragging sometimes, which caused me to just stand still or to trip and stumble. "A determined spirit" was helping me to learn, no matter what condition I was in, to be content. Because of God's Word, my testimonies for Him grew stronger and stronger.

During this season, Stacey and Ashley were saved and water baptized at Parker Memorial. We all were involved in Bible study and other ministries because we were a family that loved the Lord. I was in the following ministries: hospitality, follow-up, women's, drama, and two choirs. I was head of the drama ministry for two years. Even so, the choirs were the most taxing physically for me, but I loved to sing. Many, many times my mobility was very difficult and I was dragging a lot, but I made it by God's grace and I still praised Him. When I initially joined the choir, I was able to march in, stand for a long period of time, rock, sway, and play my tambourine. By the time we left in April 1994, I had to be escorted to the choir stand, holding on to my husband's arm. I also sat until the choir marched in. Then I would stand as long as I could. Sometimes I would have to sit while the choir stood singing, but I kept on singing even though I was sitting. When my balance was off, I would fall to the side or fall down when I was clapping my hands or swaying. "A determined spirit" would not let me give up. I would laugh to myself and think, *I'm singing praises to God, and I'm here to glorify Him.* If I had a commitment, I was there and accounted for. I knew that God didn't place me in that church body to sit on the pew. He wanted me to be a worker in His vineyard and I gave my best service. "For of Him and through Him and to Him are all things, to whom be glory forever" (Rom. 11:36).

While a member of this church, I grew in the Word of God. I learned how to read and study the Bible, and how to use other references to aid in Bible study. I learned how to develop my personal "quiet time" with the Lord, how to pray for others, how to testify, how to share the plan of salvation, and how to raise my hands and praise the Lord. I'm thankful to all the saints who prayed for me, encouraged me, helped me when I needed helping, and loved me just for being a child of God. When I had to go through steroid treatments, this church family encouraged me to keep pressing on. They got to see me when I was dragging and not up to par and when I was energized. I'm thankful that God allowed my light to shine and that I always had a testimony for Him.

We met some strong soldiers for the Lord while at Parker Memorial, men and women who had the courage and holy boldness to stand in His righteousness. I'm glad God allowed us a season with them, a number of whom we still count it a privilege to call dear friends. I'll never forget the many positive memories of our time there. I especially remember the first women's retreat I attended, where hands were laid on me and I was anointed with oil.

Women's Retreat

I had never been on a women's retreat before. The first retreat was held at a conference center in Richmond, Virginia on a Friday and Saturday in August 1991. Approximately 75 women attended. At that time I was able to walk well with a cane. No other physical aid was needed. I had fasted and prayed that God would sustain me from the beginning of the retreat to the end. On that retreat, two sisters in Christ asked me if they could anoint me with oil and pray over me. I said yes. This would be the second time in my life that this had ever been done. What a time, what a time! The presence of the Lord was in that room that night. Afterward I was renewed spiritually and felt "a determined spirit" was even more determined to run the race of life, as recorded in Hebrews 12:1, "...let us run with endurance the race that is set before us."

My second retreat experience was at the women's re-treat of August 1993, in Harper's Ferry, West Virginia. The following is my journal entry from that experience, dated August 19, 1993:

I'm going on the women's retreat from my church. Praise God! Today is the day. When this retreat started to be promoted, I knew I was going. I knew no matter what physical state I was in, I was going. Of course the adversary (satan) tried to bombard my mind with negative thoughts like, "You're not going; it's going to be too hot"; "You'll need the wheelchair. Who's going to push you?"; "There might be a lot of walking," etc. I still knew I was go-ing, that I had to go! I wanted to prove that we are capable of bearing one another's burdens, just as we are instructed to do in Galatians 6:2. My sisters in Christ did just that, from the time John dropped me off at the church until I was returned home by a sister two days later.

When we left the church the air conditioning on the bus was not working. I should have ridden in the church van, but I didn't want to waste my en-ergy, so I stayed put. We were given a "traveling mercies" prayer by a deacon, and we were on our way. As we traveled, the air conditioning never came on, so we opened the windows that could be opened. Finally, we arrived. We unloaded and got our room assignments. The wheelchair was gotten for me, and I was wheeled to my room. The whole highlight of this retreat was God speaking to me. I felt God allowed me to go to the mountain, so He could speak to me. On Thursday night, an evangelist spoke to the group. Afterward there was a praying and healing service. Sisters were prayed over and "laying on of hands" took place. There were deliverances all around. I had hands laid on me, and I was prayed over. However, I still was not able to run or jump. I began thinking about how I've had the prayer of faith prayed over me, been anointed with oil, and had hands laid on me, yet physical disabilities are still manifested. I said to myself, "I know it's not my lack of faith. I have faith, and it just gets greater and greater!" So I had just accepted my state as God's will. Well, when I returned to my room, I expressed how I felt to some sisters visiting my room. When my roommate Sherry came in, we talked and I shared with her how I felt. I told Sherry I felt she was my soulmate because so many times our thoughts seemed to come from the same sheet of music. We finally retired for the night.

Friday morning I got up, as did Sherry. She went running. I knelt beside my bed and prepared to do my devotions. First, I prayed, thanking my Father for a new day and for keeping us safe through the night. I next opened my *Daily Bread* and what was the title but, "Angel in a Wheelchair." Awesome! It was about a male construction worker who contracted multiple sclerosis and now considers himself a guardian angel of the disabled. I read the Scripture reference before reading the story and I was directed to Second Corinthians 12:1-10, where Paul prayed to have the thorn in his flesh removed.

God was telling me the same thing He told Paul, "My grace is sufficient for you, for My strength is made perfect in weakness" (see 2 Cor. 12:9). All I could do was thank God and cry! He knew everything I was going through physically and what I was wrestling with in my mind. He was right there with me.

My attendance at the women's retreats serve as a reminder of my physical well being at the time, and they contributed in a major way to my spiritual well being. I thank God for even then molding "a determined spirit."

Chapter 17

Chiropractor Consulted

"For I will restore health to you and heal you of your wounds," says the Lord.

Jeremiah 30:17a

Chiropractic care became a part of my health care regimen in 1990. The following is an account from my journal, dated August 31, 1990:

I don't feel that I have to accept my multiple sclerosis degenerative course. I'm going to continue to fight and seek healthy options. I want options whereby I won't have to resort to drugs like prednisone, but rather use methods through which my body can heal itself through regeneration. I want natural, drug-free courses of action. Oh yes, I have "a determined spirit." I believe that if your mental, spiritual, and physical beings are in balance with each other, you can't help but be healed. My goal is to get my physical being in balance with the other two.

With this goal in mind, I followed the advice of my sister Kaye to see her chiropractor. She had briefed him about my struggles with MS and he wanted to do a consultation with me and an examination. He had experience in treating MS patients. So I thought, *Why not? It can't hurt!* Besides, Kaye highly recommended this doctor and I trusted her judgment.

When Kaye first said the word *chiropractor*, I associated it with *backs*. I thought that a chiropractor was someone you went to see when you had a back problem. I had MS, what could he do for that? I really knew little about the contribution chiropractic medicine could make toward preventive health maintenance. Still, I was intrigued enough to see a chiropractor, so I asked Kaye to make me an appointment.

August 31, 1990, was the day. Kaye's doctor was in New York so we drove to the "Big Apple"—John, Stacey, and I. We dropped Ashley off at Mom's on the way out. What a beautiful day! We prayed for traveling mercies before we left home, so we knew God was with us. There was no inclement weather, just plenty of sunshine and heat.

Thank the Lord, we made it to New York by 12:00 noon. I still had an hour before my appointment, so we began looking for Kaye's job site. Then we found a place to park. "John, there's a parking lot not full," I said. We pulled in, got our claim ticket and walked to Kaye's building. The chiropractor was located in her building. It gave us a chance to see her office, which she was in the process of moving to her home. She's a self-employed organizational development consultant. We finally left her office and went to the chiropractor appointment.

I signed in and was taken to his consultation office to talk. He wanted me to understand the aim of chiropractic care and the nature of the treatment. I believe very much in letting the body function and heal itself naturally, as much as possible, so we came from the same perspective on this issue. He said to me, "Chiropractic is a scientifically sound and time-proven natural way to health." He went on to say, "by gentle manipulation of specific bones (vertebrae) that make up the spine, pressure can be relieved off of the nerves." This treatment process is called an *adjustment*. He told me the adjustment would sound like bones cracking, but it would just be air escaping. Chiropractors want you to understand the nature of their treatment as well as what *chiropractic* means. I learned that the word is Greek and means, "done by the hands."

He explained and demonstrated how the position of the spine can rest on various nerves and cause health problems when it is out of alignment. One problem I was having at that time was the inability to urinate when the urge was there. He explained that the spine might be resting on the nerves that send the impulses to the brain telling the bladder to function. He ran his hands along my spine and said he could feel where it was out of alignment. He recommended an adjustment. That day was my first visit ever to a chiropractor and I received my first adjustment.

The chiropractor recommended that I go home and locate a chiropractor near me. He said, "I will send you a recommendation for a doctor and a nutritional guide. Good nutrition and eating the proper foods play a vital role in the healing process." I felt the day was very rewarding and informative. I decided to seek a chiropractor when I got home. I thanked God for the opportunity and for the suggestion of my sister.

The New York doctor referred me to Dr. Peter McPartland. I had my first visit with him on September 11, 1990, which consisted of the following: a consultation, an examination, and X-rays. On September 12, John and I went back to find out the X-ray results and hear his recommendation. He said his overall objective would be to relieve pressure the spine was placing on the nerves. He too explained and demonstrated how the improper alignment of the spine can cause certain health problems. The first area of concentration was my neck. He gave me my first treatment—a neck adjustment, machine therapy, and traction. I agreed to go three times a week to start. I had a lot of work to do and knew that it would not occur overnight. The treatment didn't hurt and the traction felt good. I could have laid there all evening. That night I wrote the following in my journal:

> Thank You, Lord, for opening these doors for me. Healing is eminent. I claim the victory through Jesus Christ.

During my initial chiropractic care, I went three times a week. Then I went twice a week, then once a week, then once a month. But I've found I need to go at least twice a month for optimal benefit. Perhaps this is due to the effect of MS on my mobility over the past few years. When I first started going to Dr. McPartland, I did not need to use a cane to walk to his office from where I parked. As time progressed, I needed the aid of a cane to reach his office. Since January 1994, I have used a wheelchair to get from the van to his office. There have been times when I just couldn't schedule an appointment because of impaired mobility. I need someone to accompany me to assist with the wheelchair. I often take Stacey and Ashley to help me with the wheelchair when John or someone else is unavailable. The girls love to go because then they can get an adjustment too. God is so good!

I am still being treated by the same chiropractor. I regularly receive adjustments, but I haven't received heat therapy and traction since 1991. Dr. McPartland is a caring and concerned chiropractor. I value and appreciate our relationship very much.

Chapter 18

Time to Move Again

For in Him we live and move and have our being.
                                                    Acts 17:28a

As I reflect back, I am thankful to God for allowing us to experience the house on Kalmia. I always believed that He had taken us to the "mountaintop," a house on a hill— or as one friend described it, "the castle on Kalmia." However, after residing there for two years, I realized that it was time to return to level ground. It was time to move again! The main steps of the home on Kalmia had become difficult to climb. When we moved there, the steps were not a major concern. But by the end of 1990, my circumstances had changed.

On January 2, 1991, I found myself in the neurologist's office again. Even with the anticipation of moving, I had improved since my last visit. Thank You, Lord. I was experiencing numbness from the waist to the knees, but I'd had numbness somewhere on my body from the very beginning of the MS journey. I know that it is just an annoyance, rather than a debilitating symptom. On examination, I was still having a spastic paraparetic (heaviness) gait. A new symptom to report this visit had to do with my urination. I would have the urge to go, but when I would try to do so, nothing would happen. The bladder would be full, but the message would not be transmitted in a timely manner. It was frustrating. There was even an experience of incontinence (losing control). I had a urine culture taken and an assessment of my bladder would be done. I made light of the matter and said that if I had to wear a diaper of some sort, I would, believing that it would not come to that. Overall, I was feeling good, and it had been a week since completing steroid treatment. "A determined spirit" reminded me of how far I had come and that God was still my refuge and strength, a very present help in the time of trouble.

We called our realtor and began the process of searching for a home on a flat lot, with few or no steps. The ideal house would be a rambler with all the rooms on the same floor, sitting on a full basement. John was shown all kinds of houses, but ramblers were few and far between in the area where we wanted to live. We prayed and earnestly sought the Lord's guidance. We finally decided on a split level house. It was on a flat lot and had fewer steps. I was familiar with a split level because I had grown up in one from the eighth grade through college. I was excited about it. The day I was supposed to see the house, I had prayed that God would show me a sign if that was the one we were supposed to have. He did just that. The lady who owned the house was disabled and had done a stitched-art Scripture from the Bible that said, "God will take care of you." That was my confirmation. John liked the house, recognizing that we needed to remodel the kitchen and do some other renovations inside. It made a big difference not to have to climb as many steps as I did in the Kalmia house. The girls liked the house as well. As long as they could have their own bedrooms and a playroom, they were happy.

Moving day was July 5, 1991. We utilized a moving company this time around, for we had increased our furniture in the Kalmia house. Even though this house was just around the corner from the other one, it took all day to move us. Finally settled in, we have made this house a home through God's grace and "a determined spirit."

Chapter 19

Hospital Stay Triggered by Heat

Behold, You desire truth in the inward parts, and in the hidden part You will make me to know wisdom.

Psalm 51:6

We hadn't been in our new home long before I had a hospital stay. The adversary was on my case. This day's story is taken from my journal entry written July 19, 1991, the day after the hospital admittance.

I got up at 7:00 a.m., put on my exercising attire, and went to the basement. I had two goals to accomplish: morning devotions and stationary bicycling. First, I talked with God, read out loud from *The 39 Stripes of Jesus,* and read from *Our Daily Bread.* Next, I rode the bike 4.3 miles in 20 minutes. I felt great!

I went upstairs and called Ashley to breakfast, which was Alphabets, her favorite, and a cup of "Five Alive" juice. I then fixed my breakfast, one egg over-easy on a raisin English muffin and a glass of Five Alive. Ashley wanted to paint on her easel. I told her to wait until we got back from my hair appointment. She was unhappy, so I held, hugged, and talked to her. I also gave her some of my breakfast. She cheered up and decided that she would like an egg too. I fixed it. Then I went upstairs, showered, and dressed. I told Ashley to get dressed with something very cool. She did very well in this endeavor. Then we were ready to go to my 10:30 a.m. hair appointment.

When I was paying my hair charge, I noticed that both my legs were extremely numb. I thought to myself, *Gee, my legs have been numb before, but not this numb.* Well, when Ashley and I hit the outside, as I walked I felt that I wasn't going to make it to the van. I said to Ashley, "I don't think I can make it." Ashley said, "Mommy, I'll carry your purse and hold your hand." She was already carrying her backpack that held about four books. Not only did she carry her load, but mine too, and she held my hand. We made it to the van. I proceeded to my doctor's office on 19th Street in N.W. Washington, to pick up my necklace I had left there on Monday. Afterward, I left that building and walked part of the block looking for the men's shoe store that used to be across the street. It was closed, so I turned around and proceeded back to the parking lot. En route we stopped at a hot dog stand, got two hot dogs and two cokes. We got in our van and drove home.

When we arrived, Ashley was anxious to paint. I, on the other hand, was praying to make it from the van to inside the house. As soon as I got out of the van, I started shaking and shivering profusely. We made it into the kitchen, and I immediately sat in a chair. I tried to call John on his private number but got no answer. Ashley then again asked to paint, so I told her to get her things.

Meantime I called Mom and asked her why I was shivering. I told her I couldn't stop shaking. She said it was nerves. She asked where I was. I said in the kitchen. She said for me to try to get to my bed and then call her. I struggled to my bed, still shaking profusely. Meanwhile Ashley came up to the room, listening at the door I had shut lightly. I called Mom, and I recapped to her the activities up to that point. Then I started to cry because this had never happened to me before and I was tired of battling MS and not being able to do the things I was used to automatically doing. I told her Ashley wanted to paint, yet I didn't have the strength to get her things and set her up. She told me to cry it out and that I was going to be all right. She asked if I wanted her to come over, and I said, "No," because I knew she was waiting for a refrigerator to be delivered. She said to bring Ashley to my room and get under the covers.

After I hung up with her, I called Ashley, but she wouldn't come to me. I stopped crying and held out my shaking arms to her. She finally came. I held her and talked to her. I told her how much I loved her but that I didn't have the strength to get her easel right now and to please let me rest right then. I asked her, "What's wrong? Is it that you can't paint now?" She shook her head no. She said, "I heard you talking to Grandmom and say 'I don't think Ashley will understand,' but I do understand. I just want you to stop shaking." I told her that I would.

The phone rang, and it was Virginia. She asked what was happening and I told her. She said I needed to raise my body temperature and she was on her way over. I cried again, and for a few moments I asked God, "Why this trial?" I remembered that we are to count it all joy and that His strength is made perfect in weakness. I was thinking, *God is sho' nuff perfect now because I am truly weak and weakening further.*

Meanwhile I asked Ashley whether she had locked the kitchen door. I told her Aunt Virginia was coming over. Ashley told me she couldn't lock the door, so I tried to stand up to go downstairs to lock the door. I couldn't stand, so I got on my knees to crawl. I couldn't even do that. I was just too weak! I laid on the floor and cried some more. Finally, I pulled myself back to the side of my bed and told Ashley to call her Daddy by pressing his code on the phone. I was on my knees laying on the bed when she came and said, "Daddy's on the phone." I picked up. She had told John that I was shaking and couldn't stop. He asked me where I was. I told him on the side of the bed. I was really crying. He then asked if I could get in the bed. I told him I would try. He said, "I'm on my way." He then spoke to Ashley again.

The doorbell rang, and it was the mailman with a certified letter for which I needed to sign. Ashley came and relayed this information. I sent her back to bring the things upstairs so I could sign them. Ashley couldn't find a pen so she brought me a pencil and I wobbly signed it as best I could. During this process I was on the phone with my nurse practitioner at the Neurology Center. John had contacted them in regard to my present condition, so she had called just as the mailman had arrived. She asked what was going on with my body. I told her I had been in remission up until I had left the hairdresser's. She told me she would talk to Dr. Edelson and call me back.

The doorbell rang, it was Virginia. She got the heating pad going because my feet were extremely cold. She prepared tea and started to spoon feed me. I started to stop shivering and shaking. Virginia's theory was that my messages to the brain weren't working fast enough to tell the body how to cool itself in the heat. Going from the air conditioning environment to the heat environment was too fast an action for my body to respond to correctly.

The nurse practitioner called back and said that Dr. Edelson said to prescribe Valium, which would relax the nerves. She asked that I come in on Friday morning to the Chevy Chase office, and if I was still having problems, the steroid treatment would be started. I said okay.

After talking with her I started having a severe headache. It was hard to keep my eyes open, so I started napping. Mom arrived as I was napping and crying. I could feel her rubbing my face. I opened my eyes. John arrived, and Mom went out of the room. I told him, "My head hurts so bad, please give me two Tylenols." I was crying again, and I remember telling him, "I'm tired of fighting multiple sclerosis. You deserve a better wife." He said with holy boldness, "Stop talking like that. You have to fight. Stacey and Ashley need you!"

He said he was going to take my temperature. It was 103.4 degrees so he called the Neurology Center, and they told him to take me to George Washington University Hospital; so no Tylenol was given to me. He had to pull me up to a sitting position because I didn't have the strength to do it. He put my shoes on and went to stand me up, but I couldn't. My legs were like spaghetti. I couldn't feel my feet, or the floor. John picked me up and carried me down the steps into the van. What strength he has, in more ways than one.

On to George Washington University Hospital Ashley, Mom, John, and I went. When we got there, we had to go through the emergency registration process in which they gave me two ID bracelets on my wrist. Once checked in, I awaited a doctor and a space. They finally rolled me in.

I was examined, blood was taken, and I was put on an IV. The medical team believed that I had a bacterial or a viral infection. Any type of infection in the body can cause an exacerbation of the MS. This was what was happening. The fever was a signal to check for an infection, as was the headache. The doctor assigned to me wanted to have a spinal tap done to rule out spinal meningitis. The withdrawal of fluid was attempted twice, but each time, blood got into the spinal fluid extraction. This voided the test. I told them they weren't sticking me again. I was finally diagnosed with a viral infection and remained in the hospital two-and-one-half days. I told the attending physician I had to be home by Sunday because my daughter was being baptized at church.

Before I was released, the attending physician suggested I be given a prescription for prednisone. I conveyed to the neurologist that I did not need nor desire the steroid. I had gotten my mobility back, and I didn't want to take that medication for naught. I came home with no medication.

I learned a valuable lesson from this experience. That lesson was to be cognizant of the temperature in hot weather. When it's above 85 degrees, my activities for the day should be severely curtailed and I should exercise wisdom. The best scenario is to stay in an air conditioned environment. The day I went to the hairdresser, it was 100 degrees in Washington, D.C. I thank God for teaching me what I needed to know. I had operated that day through my will, not His.

Chapter 20

Neurologist's Evaluations

*Let us hold fast the confession of our hope without waver-
ing, for He who promised is faithful.*

Hebrews 10:23

The following is the summary of office visits with my
neurologist, from July 1991 to July 1994.

July 1991

I saw Dr. Edelson after my hospital experience. I was
moving right along with my cane. My only complaint was
fatigue. He recommended an oral medication, but I chose
not to try it for a possible side effect was liver problems. I
said, "No thank you. I'll just be tired."

I had another exacerbation only a few days after this
office visit. However, I was determined not to take steroids, but to just wait as long as I could. I wrote the following in my journal in August 1991:

So many things have occurred since January 1984.
Through it all, I can still say, "Thanks be to God, for
He has kept me." Through my trials, through my
tribulations, good times and bad times, I still love
my Father God. He is so good. I'm just so glad He's

head of my life. I love Him so much. I know that it's not by my own strength that I keep running the race, but by His.

December 1991

I saw Dr. Edelson on December 30. He gave the following synopsis:

> In general, Ms. Moore looks good, probably because of the weight loss. Her situation is now showing residual chronic findings, and I do not see a need for steroids at this time. We are going to repeat an MRI scan and compare it to that of 1985 to get a better feel for progression of her disease. If there is significant progression, I may feel stronger about having her get a second opinion, given how many acute and remitting episodes she has had in the past several years.

January 1992

I had my second MRI examination taken on January 6. The results were relayed to me later in the month. I still had lesions on my brain that confirmed the demyelinating disease of multiple sclerosis. But I thanked God that it had not gotten worse.

May 1992

I visited Dr. Edelson on May 18. My left leg was dragging and very weak. I used a cane and had difficulty walking without it. I had a severe gait problem. It was determined that I would do the Solu-Medrol treatment for three days followed by a 15-day prednisone taperdown course. I did well with the treatment and it sustained me until October.

October 1992

I called the neurologist on October 8. I was experiencing difficulty with balance, and my legs felt numb and heavy. Most definitely my walking was difficult and I had to rely on my cane. I received the same steroid treatment I had in May, on October 12, 13, and 14.

December 1992

I saw Dr. Edelson on December 9, and I relayed to him that the treatment received in October had not resulted in much improvement. To me it seemed that my body was becoming immune to the steroids. Dr. Edelson recommended that I see a physical therapist to see if any suggestions could be made to improve the gait.

I did consult a physical therapist, and he suggested exercises I could do using an elastic band and crossover walking routines. They have helped.

April 1993

I saw Dr. Edelson on April 9. I was walking with a cane. I had been having dizzy spells, which the neurologist felt was being caused by a virus. My general practitioner had prescribed a medication to ingest. It was working somewhat. I had gait difficulties and fatigue. During this visit the drug Beta Interferon, a future development, was mentioned. The doctor felt that I was a good candidate for this drug because I had relapsing-remitting MS.

May 1993

This office visit with Dr. Edelson was a follow-up to the October steroid treatment. I had completed the course, and the dizziness experienced at the time of the last office visit had remitted. Praise God! Even though my right leg was still dragging, my strength in my upper extremities was good. I focused on the good.

October 1993

After my follow-up visit in May, I had another exacerbation. A Solu-Medrol treatment was given, and the follow-up visit from that treatment course was set for October. I was doing somewhat better, although I had had an exacerbation that primarily affected my right leg.

February 1994

Back again in Dr. Edelson's office, I had just finished a course of Solu-Medrol in January. It hadn't helped very much. I could barely walk without assistance, even though a year ago I could walk very well with my cane. I was now using a wheelchair to get places of any distance, such as to this office visit. My cousin Delores drove me that day. I felt like there was no need to keep taking steroids if they weren't helping; maybe my body needed a rest from them. I didn't want to incur other problems (side effects). This was Dr. Edelson's report that day: "Her main problem is gait. I think basically what we are seeing in the past year is that bit by bit, she is slowly getting worse." Even with this scenario of progressing disability, I told Dr. Edelson when he mentioned Betaseron, the new MS drug approved by the Food and Drug Administration on March 23, 1993, for relapsing-remitting MS, that I wanted no part of it. This drug treatment requires injections underneath the skin every other day to be dispensed through an equal access program. It is not a cure, but data showed a reduction in the accumulation of new brain lesions as seen in the MRI scans. It is a bioengineered copy of a natural body substance.

July 1994

I was in Dr. Edelson's office to give him an update of MS activity since the last visit. There were no MS changes, only a turning outward of the right foot. This manifestation was causing a few inconveniences like pressing the gas pedal when I drove, pressing the piano pedal, and riding my stationary bicycle. I asked him if he thought physical therapy would help? He said probably not because it was caused by spasticity.

He asked if I had heard from Berlex regarding Betaseron. I told him that I had received a call from them, but told them that I didn't want to do it. I didn't want a new drug, I just wanted to keep exercising my faith for healing. I really wanted to trust God solely. If He spoke to me and told me that I'm to use Betaseron, then in obedience I would do it. "My grace is sufficient," is the message I kept receiving at that date.

Chapter 21

Sources of Strength

And we know that all things work together for good to those who love God....

Romans 8:28

Living with my decision to trust God stretches my faith daily. I have utilized several sources in this growth process; let me focus on three.

God's Word

First and foremost, God's Word nourishes my faith. It is my main source of strength. I need it everyday! I'm so thankful that I had to go through a pruning process to come to that conclusion. "All Scripture is given by inspiration of God, and is profitable for doctrine, for reproof, for correction, for instruction in righteousness" (2 Tim. 3:16). I didn't understand what this Scripture meant, until 1990. I learned as I attended Bible study regularly. I was so excited about God's Word. I just couldn't seem to get enough. I was under excellent teaching, and like a sponge, I was steadily soaking it up. I prayed to be obedient to the Scripture that says, "Be diligent to present yourself approved to God, a worker who does not need to be ashamed, rightly dividing the word of truth" (2 Tim. 2:15).

My first Bible acquisitions occurred in February 1990. They consisted of a NIV Study Bible and New King James Bible. After being in Bible study a few months, I also needed to purchase a concordance, a commentary, a Bible dictionary, and various other reference sources. My growing library included not only books, but teaching and preaching cassette tapes as well. What a blessing! "A determined spirit" had embarked on the journey to understand God's Word through the navigation of the Holy Spirit.

After regular participation in Bible study, I realized how necessary "quiet time" with God was. We not only have to talk to God, but we have to listen so He can speak to us. I'm a morning person, so I implemented my "quiet time" in the morning. It has truly been a blessing.

At the end of August 1991, I was reading a little book called *By Jesus' 39 Stripes We Were Healed,* by Walter A. Straughan. This book came to me through my husband who heard the author speak to a Bible study group at his workplace. On August 27, Mr. Straughan spoke on the subject of "healing," for he had been healed from multiple sclerosis. Imagine the excitement my husband had over hearing this man's testimony. It was still evident when he gave me the book. I'm so thankful to God for His will that day, that John would be in that Bible study meeting. It was a confirmation of the power of God's Word.

Straughan's book contains Scriptures from God's Word and confessions based on the Scriptures that are relevant to healing. God's Word is powerful! I can't say it better than Hebrews 4:12 (NIV) says it, "For the word of God is living and active. Sharper than any double-edged sword, it penetrates even to dividing soul and spirit, joints and marrow; it judges the thoughts and attitudes of the heart." I was blessed to receive it for it centered my mind on God's Word, not the suffering I was experiencing. I came to realize that I had to believe and not doubt God's Word. I knew that faith is "being sure of what we hope for and certain of what we do not see" (Heb. 11:1 NIV).

At the beginning of *By Jesus' 39 Stripes We Were Healed,* it states:

> "The Bible says that God sent His Word and healed them all. The *key* to receiving healing in our minds and bodies is in the Word of God. We have to hear God's Word so faith will come into our hearts, and we have to confess God's Word before we can release faith. Also, we have to act on God's Word as much as we can at all times. If we are confessing and acting on God's Word we are in 100 percent faith, and we will always receive the answer to our prayer from our heavenly Father."[1]

I believed this paragraph and knew that my work was cut out for me. "So then faith comes by hearing, and hearing by the word of God" (Rom. 10:17). During my acceptance period, I held fast to the belief that God *would* heal me, but I'm clear in my mind that He already has. What I came to understand through studying God's Word is that when He went to the cross, He bore all of our sicknesses in His body, and at that point I was healed (1 Pet. 2:24). Sickness does not come from God because Christ redeemed us from the curse of Old Testament law (Gal. 3:13). However, I believe that He allows satan to test us through trials and tribulations so that He will be glorified. Through the testing, we are drawn to Him. I must always remember that satan only comes to steal, kill, and destroy (Jn. 10:10). He's relentless in trying to convince me that there's no hope for my MS, but God's Word confirms otherwise. "A determined spirit" believes, "I've got the victory because Jesus paid the price for me." I must hold fast to First Peter 2:24, which tells me that by His stripes I'm healed, regardless of what symptoms manifest themselves in my body.

"A determined spirit" has learned that, despite our circumstances, we must be consistent in studying God's Word and "...fix our eyes on Jesus, the author and perfecter of our faith, who for the joy set before Him endured the cross..." (Heb. 12:2 NIV). I didn't understand the Scripture from Proverbs 4:20-22 (KJV) that says: "My son, attend to my words.... Let them not depart from thine eyes; keep them in the midst of thine heart. For they are life unto those who find them, and *health* to all their flesh." But I understand it now! Satan will feed your mind thoughts like, "I don't feel like reading the Word; I'm tired"; "you're getting worse"; "what's the point"; and similar negative messages.

I was so inspired by God's Word that I held a women's Bible study group at my home in the Fall of 1991. There were eight of us and we did a study called, "When A

Woman Takes God At His Word" by Pat Baker. That undertaking was in the will of God, and it proved to be a tremendous blessing to all of us. I'm thankful to have been a vessel for His service. It was in this Bible study that the question was asked, "What dream do you have?" My dream was to write a book.

The following song sums up my thankfulness for God's Word. It is entitled "God's Word Shall Never Pass Away."[2] I would just like to quote two verses:

> His Word is hidden in my heart,
> > and it's ever there to stay;
> All hell cannot make it depart,
> > for it shall not pass away.
> God's Word shall never pass away,
> > it shall ever more abide;
> Until all ages come and go,
> > and I'm safely by His side.

Music

God's Word was also given to me through song lyrics. I like to sing, play the piano, and actively listen to music. No matter what you're going through, there is a song that can lift your spirit. I love music, and I like to read, study, and learn the words. When I liked to party and dance, worldly music was my focus, but having restored my fellowship with Christ, I desire to do what Romans 12:2 says, "And do not be conformed to this world, but be transformed by the renewing of your mind...."

I like to play the piano, and I had the desire to play it better. Every time Stacey and Ashley would go to their piano lessons, I wanted to be taking lessons too. "A determined spirit" was telling me that I could do it! I prayed and asked God if He would allow me to take piano lessons. I was inspired and commenced in the fall of 1991, resuming in the music book I stopped in as a child. I was so excited. I looked forward to practicing. Arrangements were made with the instructor of my children, Dr. Hattie Davis, to take piano lessons for 30 minutes, one day a week. As they began their lessons for the year, so did I.

My lesson was every Tuesday, in the morning. I looked forward to it every week, and I loved it. When I talked to Dr. Davis regarding lessons, I told her that I had multiple sclerosis and sometimes my hands worked well and sometimes they didn't. I told her that I would be undertaking this endeavor through faith. Being a saved Christian, she understood. The MS sometimes affected my ability to move my fingers on the keyboard with strength because of spasticity and weakness. She gave me practice exercises to help strengthen the weak fingers. Another problem I had was pressing and holding the sustaining pedal on the piano. Nevertheless, I was committed, and I knew I would persevere to the end. Dr. Davis saw how determined I was to do the best I could do. She praised me when I had a good practice week, which resulted in a good lesson, and she encouraged me when I was experiencing difficulty. She said to me one day, "You really get into your music and feel it. I can tell by your playing." She hit the nail on the head, that's exactly the effect music has on me. It quickens, relaxes, and revitalizes me. Whether I'm singing, playing, or listening to it, I love music. I especially like praise and worship music, gospel music, Christian jazz, instrumental music, and classical music. I enjoy songs as well as instrumentals. There is a time and a place for each.

It was April and nearing recital time. I had never participated in a piano recital, so I wanted to experience one. Dr. Davis said it was up to me if I wanted to work on a piece for the recital. I chose to do so. I practiced and practiced my piece. The day of the recital came and it was my turn. I was nervous, but I prayed and successfully completed the rendition. What a day of rejoicing that was for me. "A determined spirit" had persevered! Thank You, Lord.

I can remember the effect of religious music on me as a choir member. I gained much strength from the service of singing God's praises. One song in particular was my favorite for a long time. It was called, "For the Good of Them."[3] The lyrics are as follows:

> The race is not given to the swift nor the
>   strong
> But to the one that endureth until the end
> There'll be problems and sometimes you'll
>   walk alone
> But I know that I know that I know things will
>   work out
> Yes they will, for the good of them
> For the good of them who love the Lord.
>
> Eyes haven't seen and neither have ears heard
> The things God has prepared for them that
>   love Him
> Sometimes you have to cry and sometimes
>   you may have to walk alone
> But I know that I know that I know things will
>   work out

Yes they will, for the good of them
For the good of them who love the Lord.

No matter what the problems
You can't solve them
They will come
But don't worry
It will work out for the good of them
Who love the Lord.

That song is one of my testimonies, and whenever I led the solo, I cried and cried. I remember the Sunday Ashley was scheduled to be baptized. At rehearsal I asked to sing the solo on Sunday. That was the weekend I had been admitted to the hospital because of my reactions to the heat. I had pleaded for the doctor to let me go home because my daughter was being baptized. Well, when I walked into the church, I was overjoyed and thankful just to be alive. I came in with a pillow to place behind my back—which was sore from the lumbar punctures—and sat down. The next thing I knew someone was handing me the microphone to sing that song. That was it! The Spirit of God was upon me and tears flooded my being. I had just come out of the hospital, my child was being baptized, and my family and friends were present. I know the Holy Spirit had spoken to the choir's pianist regarding the song. The Holy Spirit was moving in church that Sunday, and I rejoiced in His presence. It was wonderful!

I utilize a tape of instrumental meditation music during many of my "quiet time" sessions. After seeking the presence of the Holy Spirit and meditating on the awesomeness of God, "a determined spirit" is prepared to confront the demands of the day. I'm so thankful for music.

Exercising

I have always enjoyed exercise. Having multiple sclerosis has required me to cut back my routine, but I have not had to stop altogether. Although my stamina isn't as great as it used to be, I exercise when I can and do the best that I can. Some days I just don't have the strength or balance to undertake the routine. Then there are days "a determined spirit" goes for it, using wisdom, the Word, and prayer. I do not want my muscles to atrophy (shrink) or weaken from lack of use. The purpose of exercising is to improve my all-around conditioning. With such improvement, enhanced strength is possible.

People with MS are so often told to rest and not overexert themselves. As a result, the fear of fatigue becomes too self-restrictive. I believe that people with disabilities should not be crippled by fear—there is nothing to be afraid of. According to Second Timothy 1:7, "For God has not given us a spirit of fear, but of power and of love and of a sound mind." This means I exercise using my common sense. I rest when I need to, and if that means "no exercising today," then I don't do it. It also means that I do nothing in my own strength, but everything in the strength of the Lord. So I pray before I exercise and thank the Lord for the opportunity to do so. Then I ask Him to help me. It's that simple. I personalize Philippians 4:13 by saying, "I *will* do all things through Christ who strengthens me." If it's a nonenergized day, I don't sweat it for I know the day will come when I will be energized. That's "a determined spirit."

For Christmas 1990, John gave me a wrapped box. Inside was the picture of a Flex cross-training exercise apparatus. I received the gift in January 1991. Yeah! I wanted a set that would allow me to exercise various parts of my body, focusing on maintenance of strength. I've been working out, as my body allows, ever since. I now own two pieces of apparatus: a stationary exercycle and the Flex. I also like to lift free-standing weights, and I own a few of them as well. Onward and upward!

One should also exercise spiritually with God's Word. Listening to Scriptures recorded on tape or in the lyrics of songs allows us to exercise our mental and spiritual selves just as we exercise our physical bodies. I find that a good time to think about and meditate on memorized Scriptures is when I'm exercising. God's Word is medicine to all our flesh.

Chapter 22

My Husband and My Children

Every good gift and every perfect gift is from above, and comes down from the Father of lights....

James 1:17

Multiple sclerosis has certainly affected my relationships with my husband and my children. When I met my husband I had no symptoms of MS, but after he asked me to marry him, my symptoms began to show up. John could have said, "Forget the marriage," and exited my life, but he didn't. That confirmed to me that he wanted me as his wife, and come what may, he would not desert me. He lives MS with me every day, knowing from whence I came yet not knowing what my future will be. He's not worried about the future because he knows God holds it. We live one day at a time, praising the Lord anyhow. As for my children, they have never known me without MS. I would like to share how blessed and thankful I am to have the family that I do.

The Living Bible says, "The man who finds a wife finds a good thing; she is a blessing to him from the Lord"

(Prov. 18:22). When we wed, we vowed to love and honor each other through sickness and through health. My multiple sclerosis is just a test of that commitment. I pray daily that even with my affliction, I will be the best wife I can be to my husband. I believe that prayer is answered every day, through the grace of God.

What is required in our marriage is patience and understanding in the management of MS. These two qualities are necessary for any marriage, so ours is not unique in that respect. What is unique is the changing of roles from time to time. Sometimes John has to do things I would normally do, like grocery shopping, laundry, and other home-related tasks, due to my experiencing weakness or other symptoms. He usually attends to Stacey's and Ashley's cuts, scrapes, splinters, etc. when I'm unable to see clearly because of optic neuritis. In a progressive disability scenario, anything can change. Having had MS for 13 years, my ambulatory status is dependent upon help from people or assistive apparatuses.

Communication is vitally important in our marriage. I can't assume that he knows how I'm feeling or what I'm thinking. I can't shut down on him, even when it's easier not to talk sometimes. When children are in the family, it's very important to demonstrate love and understanding. Communicating effectively must be a primary goal. Children are like sponges and absorb so much, even when you think they don't.

John demonstrates how much he loves me over and over, and he says, "I love you" without hesitation. He's

flexible and giving. He carries me up or down steps sometimes, by his choosing, so that I won't have to struggle in
the ascent or descent. God really gave me a good man. He
is my biggest cheerleader and always has been. The cheer-
ing did not stop when multiple sclerosis became part of
my life. It drew us closer to God and closer to each other.
He encourages me daily. There are times when I wish he
had a wife with no affliction. There are times when I want
to get something for him, fix his plate, iron something,
etc., but he will say, "No," so I won't have to walk or maneuver steps. He has always been easy going about meals,
household chores, and other things. He never complains
if I don't feel like doing something. He doesn't have the
"E.G.O." problem, which stands for "edge God out." He's
always trying to make my life easier, even after a long day
at work. What a husband! No, I'm not the easiest person
to get along with all the time. I like to be independent and
do tasks. Even when I'm told not to do something or that
I should rest, I don't always respond appropriately. I have
my moments, and sometimes I'm just plain stubborn. I realize that I'm still maturing in my character, and John re-
alizes it too. His self-control is outstanding. He also
demonstrates the other fruit of the Spirit—love, joy, peace,
patience, and kindness—as well. We both have our moments of frustration, for me because I'm being hardheaded, for him because he's trying to conserve my
energy. We compromise many times and pray without
ceasing. I believe the hardest thing to develop is agape
love, God-like, unconditional love. The foundation of love
and respect was in place when we married, thank God. I

recognize how blessed I am to have John as my husband. "A determined spirit" helps me be the wife that I am and not hold pity parties about being a wife with multiple sclerosis. I know God orchestrated this union and fully knew the trials and circumstances we would face together.

An important element that John and I need to improve on is "getting away." We must find ways to do this in spite of my MS. It is very important that a husband and wife stay in tune with each other, which requires time alone, without the children. With the use of aids to assist me, this is possible as long as I remain ambulatory.

Our life has changed, and my husband is not the only one who has been impacted by it. Our children, Stacey and Ashley, have been affected as well. The Scripture that says, "Behold, children are a heritage from the Lord, the fruit of the womb is His reward" (Ps. 127:3) describes how I view my children. When they were babies, I realized that they were God's children and had just been placed into our care to be raised in the fear and admonition of Him. We were instructed to train them in the way they should go, so I looked forward to the challenge.

I was able to be a busy, attentive mother when they were in the infant and toddler stages. I was stronger and more energetic. I was able to lift them, walk without assistance, and didn't experience ongoing optic neuritis and other symptoms. I was able to attend to their needs because I was in remission more than I was out of remission. From their observation things didn't change until age 4, when they started going to school. They wondered why I didn't work outside the home, why fluorescent lights bothered my eyes, why I couldn't run, and why I got tired quickly. I answered their questions as they arose. They also were questioned by their peers about why I had to use a cane, or why I walked funny. They learned how to answer such questions and not be embarrassed by my MS.

Both of them went to the same school until Stacey entered second grade. John and I decided that we wanted them to have the foundation of a Christian school education. We desired for them to have Bible in their curriculum, for we both knew that God's Word stands forever. We wanted them to learn Bible truths right along with the other academic subjects. We decided to put Stacey at Forcey Christian School in Silver Spring, Maryland and keep Ashley at Shepherd Park Elementary School in Washington until she finished kindergarten. This meant picking Ashley up at 2:30 p.m. in order to get Stacey at 3:00 p.m. This was the routine every day unless Stacey had a half day or a school holiday. If I had a treatment, which sometimes I did, arrangements were made to have someone else pick them up. Some days we went from school to dance or piano lessons. This was fatiguing but through God's grace "a determined spirit" made it.

When Stacey entered third grade, she and Ashley were at Forcey together. Yeah! That was a blessing. I came to realize that parenthood means sacrifices for your children, even when you don't feel like it. Both of them exited the same door when their teachers brought them outside at the end of the day, so I could get them with no problem. I was also able to help with class parties and go on field trips with them. When I was in remission the routine was easy to accomplish. When I was not, it was more of a struggle. Nonetheless, we made it through that year.

I didn't really start having trouble walking and retrieving them until 1992. Stacey was in fourth grade and Ashley was in second. Their teachers would bring them outside, and I would have to go get them. However, Ashley's grade came out on the side of the building where I parked, whereas Stacey's came out the front of the building. I had to write a letter to Stacey's teacher requesting she be allowed to leave out the side with Ashley, so they could be retrieved together. There were days when just getting out of the van to walk was tough. When it rained I had to go inside the building to retrieve them. That was a longer walk. In September 1993, I finally had to write their teachers a note to have them dismissed to walk to where I was parked, which was in the handicapped section. Stacey would go get Ashley, and then they both would come to the van together. (Stacey really began to ask questions and become concerned about MS at this time.)

I can remember going on two field trips in 1992, one with each of them. Those were to be my last field trips. I just couldn't do it anymore. The trips required real stamina, and mine was steadily lessening, even walking was becoming a struggle. I'm just glad that I did get to share that experience with them. I even got to make a presentation to their classes during Black History Month in February. I really enjoyed that and so did they.

I can honestly say that their teachers and the administration have been most understanding and helpful to me.

One rainy afternoon when I went to pick them up, an accident had occurred and stalled traffic. As a result I arrived on time, rather than a few minutes early like usual. By then all of the handicapped parking spaces had been taken by cars without handicapped stickers, so I had to park further away in non-reserved parking. I was upset at what had happened, and the next morning I wrote a note to the principal explaining the situation and asking him to please remind parents about the restriction on parking in handicapped spaces. He promptly did as I asked in the weekly newsletter to parents. I was very appreciative.

I began to see that Stacey was really being bothered by my MS and I told my mom. I'm so thankful that she suggested that I let both girls talk to a psychologist at the MS Society. It opened my eyes to see that my having MS is taxing on them as well. They have never known me without MS, but they do notice when I'm weaker or stronger. I came to understand that they are children and have feelings that they need to talk about and express on their level. The psychologist who talked to them was excellent and broke MS down so they could understand it on a child's level. He encouraged them to ask questions and to talk about anything on their minds. Stacey gave him her questions and answered his. Ashley didn't have any questions and wouldn't talk much. Both were asked to draw how they saw me and our family, with MS in the picture. Their pictures were quite revealing. The psychologist told me in private that they both have excellent perspectives regarding MS and well-thought-out plans for handling potential problems. If they are with me and something happens, they know what to do. We discussed other things as well. What a blessing! That entire session opened a lot of doors, especially the one of using the services that the MS Society offers.

Life continued, and through some weeks of family counseling with a Christian professional, Stacey began to more fully understand and accept me as I am. I coordinated the Christmas party for her class and carried it out with the help of my niece Kia. I had to use the wheelchair to get to the classroom. Stacey helped us and was real excited about me being there. All went well and we both were happy.

In 1994, John and I purposed to do more "family" things. We attended a five-week session called "Focus on the Family," which was sponsored by the MS Society, starting in May. In these sessions, the children were grouped together with an artist to do Art Therapy. The parents got to interact with other adults about issues that affect the family. The program was great because it allowed Stacey and Ashley to meet other children who had a parent with MS, and it allowed them to share their feelings about MS with other children. As for John and me, it allowed us to hear from others and share with them how MS impacts families. We were often called upon for our reaction or perspective concerning various topics of discussion since we were the "senior" couple with exposure to MS. It was the first time that any of the participants had attended a program of that kind, and each of us benefitted from the experience.

I know that our family situation will undergo many changes as MS affects our household. I know that Stacey and Ashley wish I didn't have MS, but they understand that we must deal with it through the strength of the Lord. As Stacey and Ashley mature in grace, they will come to understand what a blessing it is to have a mother with "a determined spirit." In the meantime, I keep ripening my fruit of the Spirit, especially patience and self-control.

I'm so thankful that God gave them sharp minds. John and I both give them the attention required for monitoring and helping with their homework and projects. They are excellent students and have good study habits. I value their opinions and thoughts. Some days my nerves are really tried, especially when they want to go over to "so and so's" house, or go here or go there. Nevertheless, these issues are each resolved. Thank the Lord.

There have been times when optic neuritis has affected my seeing of the colors on a traffic light clearly, so Ashley and Stacey will tell me what color it is so I'll know to stop or go. I don't know what I would do without both of them sometimes. When we have to go somewhere without John, I depend on Stacey and Ashley to help me. When we need to use the wheelchair, we have a system of counting 1–2–3 to lift it down and lift it back up into the van. It works well. When it's just Ashley and me, I enjoy the routine even more. Ashley has the gift of "helps" and loves to exercise it. She sees what I need assistance with and proceeds to help. Stacey is not as automatic in the "assisting Mom" department. She will help if asked, but Stacey does not volunteer as readily as Ashley. Perhaps this is a reflection of the difference in their ages or of their perception of my need for assistance. I don't mind asking either of them to help when necessary, but I try not to overburden them. I'm still their mother, in sickness or in health.

In addition to helping with my transportation needs, Stacey and Ashley have also assisted me by providing their shoulders to help steady my walk; their legs to retrieve or carry something for me; and their hands to help me get dressed, comb or brush my hair, etc. My MS experience affords me the opportunity to teach them to demonstrate sensitivity toward others with an illness or disability and to show compassion to those who have to use aids like a cane, walker, or wheelchair. I am confident that as a result of having to deal with my MS experience, they are developing various attributes that will enhance their characters as they mature into adulthood.

Stacey and Ashley have household tasks they are responsible for, such as tidying up their bedrooms, watering the plants, setting the table, and assisting with the dishes. We hold them accountable for performing their daily or weekly chores. Teamwork in our household is a necessity, and it is very effective. Sometimes I give them opportunities to cook and bake on their level as well as perform required household tasks. They're great at preparing their specialities. I can remember one Saturday night when they cooked dinner. Here is what I recorded in my journal:

Dec. 29, 1993. Yesterday, Stacey and Ashley fixed dinner for John, myself, Sonny, and Becky (my brother-in-law and sister). It was too cute! They had a sign on the wall naming their restaurant "California Look In." They played the roles of waitresses, with menus and everything. Stacey cut up and cooked potatoes in the oven. They were very good. They made a salad with lettuce and carrots. They made sandwiches of cheese and shaved turkey.

They let us know at the onset on the menu that a tip was required. They even gave us a bill. I was real proud of them!

That was their first time doing the whole meal, but it wasn't their last.

Over the years both girls have given me artwork at various times to convey their thoughts and feelings. What a collection I have on the walls of my office. Each picture is an inspiration in its own right. I was brought to tears by most of them, especially one in particular that was done by Ashley when she was seven. Her picture got right to the point. I was out of remission and having a hard time. She drew a picture and titled it, "Mom And Her Strugls." Then she wrote above the picture, "My Mom strugle but she prays to God and Jesus." The picture had me smiling and the sun shining. It got to the core of my being, and I cried and cried. It showed that Ashley not only understood that I was having a rough time, but that I pray to God faithfully.

There have been times when I have been tired and weak and both of them have ministered to me. Here's a day remembered in my journal:

Sunday, March 20, 1994. I got up, had my quiet time, went to the kitchen, and began to prepare dinner. After frying chicken, which requires standing off and on to check it, turn it, and remove it, I had no energy left. I knew I still had to get upstairs, shower, dress, and leave for church. As I went up the stairs my legs were heavy and weak. When I made it to my room, I fell on my knees to pray and ask God for strength. I had closed my bedroom door upon entering my room. On my knees I just started crying and saying, "Lord I can't do this anymore, I need strength. Lord, I know what Your will is for me, how am I to accomplish it? I don't have energy to pick myself up and get on the bed." I kept crying. I asked God for strength. The radio was playing gospel music and the announcer played the song "Stand Still" by the Wilmington Chester Mass Choir. The announcer then said that something in her spirit had told her to play it. That song encourages me, and when I hear it I cry and cry. Then she played it again saying the Spirit was prompting this. I knew then that God was speaking to me. I kept crying. Then she played "Focus on Heaven." Why focus on Heaven? Because Jesus is there making intercession for me. I could feel the presence of the Lord, and I was able to get up and sit on the bed. By that time the bedroom door opened and Stacey and Ashley walked in. Stacey sat on my left side and took my hand and Ashley sat on my right. It was as if Stacey was my mother. She started saying, "You can make it Mom, you can." Ashley said, "We'll help you Mom, we'll help you." God had answered my prayer. Ashley left the room. Stacey and I hugged and comforted each other, for she was crying now. We both dried our tears, and I then had strength to take my shower and get dressed.

I now recognize that my independent role has been replaced by one of dependence. Nonetheless, I am blessed!

I have three gems in my life—John, Stacey and Ashley—who help me manage in spite of my MS, and I'm so thankful to God for the family He has given me. I love them very much. Each of them encourages me in his or her own way. They are my inspiration and help me sustain "a determined spirit." Together, we will do all things through Christ.

Chapter 23

Other Relationships

And now abide faith, hope, love, these three; but the greatest of these is love.

1 Corinthians 13:13

Parents

I'm thankful to have a wonderful relationship with my parents, and I love them very much. They have been with me, praise God, through all my MS trials and tribulations. In the last six years, my dad has not been able to be as active as he was before he got sick. He still tries to do what he can, even though he was diagnosed with cancer of the liver in 1993. My dad is a trooper, and he shares with me his wisdom and insight.

It's important to know some things about my mom, in order to understand why I don't like to burden her. I call on her for assistance only when absolutely necessary. Mom is the caretaker for my dad, and she also helps my sister Virginia who has lupus. Yet, she still helps me every chance she gets. I tell her not to worry about me or feel that she has to do things for me, but she still volunteers her services. I know that being a caretaker for our family was one of the purposes God had for her. She has taken care of a lot of family members during their illnesses. She does the job well. She's an unselfish, godly woman who loves demonstrating the fruit of the Spirit. What a strong, wonderful woman! She has ills and down time too, but she recovers and continues the pattern of giving of herself.

I praise God that Mom and I have always had a close relationship. When I told her that my MS was confirmed, she immediately looked at herself to see what she could have done to prevent my having it. I told her that it's not hereditary and that it was purposed to be. She encourages me all the time and says that I am an inspiration to her because she knows I press on even with MS.

Mom helps me with Stacey and Ashley in many ways. More than once she has been a lifesaver. I'm so blessed! When I need her, I just have to call her. However, she makes herself available even when I don't call. That's my Mom.

I think one of the hardest things Mom has had to adjust to is that I'm not able to do things and go places like I used to. I used to drive over to her house and take her places in a heartbeat, but now I have difficulty walking and can't do things at the drop of a hat or for long periods of time. Just standing for short periods of time is sometimes hard. I've explained my current status to her, and she can also see and observe my difficulties. I used to be able to climb the staircase and enter Mom's front and side doors with no trouble, but now it's difficult. Sometimes it's easier for her to come to my house than for me to go to hers because of my difficulty with walking. Mom understands, and that's why she tries to carry some of my weight. I'm so grateful. Mom doesn't complain, even though she deals with arthritis daily. Initially, the hardest thing for me was to ask for help. I'm stubborn at times and just like to do things myself. I especially did not want to bother my mother. I wanted to be a servant for her, but now my life has changed.

There's one special event Mom planned and orchestrated that will be a lasting memory. It was a surprise fortieth birthday fellowship for me at my house in September 1994. What a blessed celebration! As we returned from church, the guests came out of the house and greeted me in the carport with "Happy Birthday." The buffet brunch was delicious. Only Mom! There's nobody like her. Mom is very special to me and my family.

Brothers and Sisters

I'm so glad that our parents taught their children to love one another. Being the youngest of six, I was not starved for attention. We are all different, yet still close enough to care about each other. If one of us suffers, all of us do. We have a variety of ailments in this family, nonetheless we are there for each other.

I know that my brothers and sisters were surprised when they heard that I was diagnosed with MS. Not Sharon! They prayed that it was a mis-diagnosis, and when it wasn't they prayed that it would go into remission forever. I'm sure by now they know I have "a determined spirit." They see that I live my life by faith.

Again asking for help was something I didn't want to do. I was Ms. Independent! I had to bury my pride and show that I'm not strong all the time. The day I had to hold onto Virginia, who has lupus, to help *me* walk, was a happy day. The day Becky and her husband came over to see how I was doing and I talked, cried, and felt a load lifted, was a happy day. The day I receive a telephone call from Silas Jr. or Dwight, just to say hello and see how I'm doing, is a happy day. The day Kaye calls while she's on travel for business to check on "her nieces," ask about John, and see how I'm feeling is a happy day. When I think about my brothers and sisters and know that they love and care about me, I am strengthened and encouraged. I love them very much.

My Cousin Carmen

Carmen and I have always shared a friendship above and beyond the fact that she's my cousin. When she found out I was diagnosed with MS, she was taken aback—"Miss Active Sharon," she couldn't believe it. I recently asked her what she thought and how she felt when I was diagnosed. She said that she thought about all the things I wouldn't be able to do and that had made her sad. Yet when she saw I had "a determined spirit," she got her feelings in check. She's Stacey's godmother and offered to do what she could to help me. All I ever had to do was call and ask. She's a wonderful listener and sounding board for me. Even with the responsibilities of her own family, she offers to do things for me. I love and appreciate her very much.

Friends

As I was growing up I was taught that if you want a friend, then you must be a friend. Good, faithful, committed friends are hard to come by. I know that God placed some people in my life for specific purposes, at His appointed time in my MS experience. I'm thankful for their contributions to my spiritual growth, which resulted in a more obedient walk with Christ. I've had friends and acquaintances who have impacted my life. Some have stuck with me, others have disconnected. I wonder sometimes if the ones who have disconnected did so because of my MS or because of my relationship with God. Whatever the reason may be, I am guided by Colossians 1:10 that says, "that you may have a walk worthy of the Lord, fully pleasing Him, being fruitful in every good work and increasing in the knowledge of God." I am thankful for my friends, both local and distant, who have stuck by me.

There's one person who has been an especially close friend for 12 years of my MS journey. I don't take our friendship for granted, and I'm thankful for it. Joyce and I worked at the same company, and I was her supervisor for a time. We became friends, and she never lost sight of who I am, by making the mistake of focusing on my disability. There is nothing that Joyce won't try to do for me when I need her. I only have to call her. She has a big heart and much compassion.

She has helped me with Stacey and Ashley, with cooking, cleaning—wherever the need was—innumerable times. Whenever I want to go somewhere, she'll drive me without hesitation. She has no problem with having to load up my wheelchair, push me, and assist me into our destination before parking, etc. Joyce has grown so much spiritually, and she is a prayer warrior. She comes over to pray with me and to have scriptural discussions. She encourages me all the time, because sometimes "a determined spirit" becomes weary. I'll never forget the night she refused to leave my house until I drank three 8 oz. glasses of water. I was not in the daily habit of drinking a sufficient amount of water, although I really needed to. She lectured me in love, and then had me drink the water that night. I'm so grateful because ever since then, I drink the proper amount of water with no problem. We haven't been in agreement all the time, but we're able to disagree in love. We focus on the majors and not the minors. I'm thankful to God for our friendship and for us having the same major, Jesus.

There are other special friends with servant attitudes that I'm blessed to have in my life. Some of them suffer with MS, cancer, or other illnesses. We minister to each other. I love and thank God for all of them. Family members need a break sometimes, and these faithful friends are there to help me.

The song "If I Can Help Somebody"[1] presents a worthwhile goal for each of us to strive for. I'm thankful for those who call, send cards or gifts throughout the year, visit, or extend themselves in other ways. It means so much. Their love, compassion, and interaction help to encourage and sustain "a determined spirit." Yet, in spite of it all, I've come to understand the truth in the words of the song writer who wrote, "There's not a Friend Like the Lowly Jesus, No Not One."[2]

Chapter 24

Failed Attacks of the Adversary

No weapon formed against you shall prosper....
                                        Isaiah 54:17

"A determined spirit" must put on the whole armor of God to stand against the adversary, every day. The necessary equipment is found in Ephesians 6:14-17. One day after reading this passage, I wrote the following poem, entitled "Dressed For Battle":

> Are you dressed for battle?
> Are you ready to fight?
> There's a war raging,
> you must be clothed just right.
>
> You must have on your armor,
> the Word in your heart.
> Then you can stand off Satan,
> who wants to tear you apart.
>
> You must be dressed for battle,
> having on all your gear.
> To strengthen the body,
> dismiss the fear.

Have on your belt, don't forget your breastplate.
Have on your shoes, don't leave off your shield.
Have on your helmet, and by all means
don't forget your sword.
These are all necessary to press on for the reward.

Satan awaits, he's always around,
not to pick you up, but just to keep you down.

God told us to stand, rooted and grounded,
so His Word would be applied,
implanted and not confounded.

So this is your protection,
to guard our direction.
Keep the faith, continually pray,
for to follow Christ, there is no other way.

Be strong in the Lord and in the power of His might,
With all your equipment in place, you're ready to fight!

Climb in the saddle, you're now dressed for battle.

When I start my day, I am dressed for battle, for satan tries his best to focus my mind on circumstances. I let him know very quickly that I'm in the Lord's army. I've had a number of experiences that demonstrate that God is in control of my life's situations and that I need to put on the whole armor of God to fight the adversary.

Out of Gas

It was August 1993, rush hour, and I ran out of gas on a main thoroughfare in Washington, D.C. This was a first for me. I had never run out of gas before. I'm so thankful that Stacey and Ashley were with me. We had been out all day with my cousin Delores, and I had just dropped her off at her home. I knew I needed gas, so we were on our way to the gas station. The van slowed to a stop, dead in the center of traffic. I tried to coast into a turn lane, but succeeded in getting only half of the van into the lane. I said to the girls, "Oh no, we're out of gas!" Stacey started to get upset. I told her to be cool and calm down. I got out and went to the back of the van. I started to wave my arms and shout "Help!" to no avail. I started praying, "Lord, please send me some help." I went back to the van and retrieved my cane. I called to Stacey to come to me. She came and I sent her to a house across from where we were to ask to use the phone. A woman came to her door window and told Stacey, "No." Meanwhile a man in a truck stopped and asked if I needed help. I told him I needed gas and he offered to take me to get it. He got Stacey back across the street, and he took us to get gas. The gas station had no gas can, so we had to put it in an empty antifreeze bottle. We returned to the van, put in the gas, and he followed me to the gas station. There was no doubt in my mind that this man was God-sent especially due to the response of the other people who had passed us by. To this day, I thank God for the man named Frank.

Falling

The adversary started attacking me with the "falling thing" in the fall of 1993. Whenever I fell, I recognized that it was satan trying to discourage me. It didn't work because God spoke to me and said, "Have I not commanded you? Be strong and of good courage; do not be afraid, nor be dismayed, for the Lord your God is with you wherever you go" (Josh. 1:9). Because of this medicine to my flesh, I got up each and every time I fell.

Be encouraged. If you feel that the adversary is beating up on you over and over again, know that it's his job to do so and he does it well. However, as believers we have the victory, and "No weapon formed against you shall prosper…" (Is. 54:17). Aim to become satan's biggest nightmare by confessing Jesus as your Lord and Savior every time the enemy attacks you. Hold on to the testimony of Job, "Though He slay me, yet will I trust Him" (Job 13:15). I praise God that He promised never to leave us. Over and over again I have witnessed His omnipresence. I know that He is there every time I fall because he always picks me up.

November 1993

I was in my house and walked to the coat closet to retrieve my jacket to go to a hair appointment. I went to put my hand on the wall at the closet, missed it, and fell into the bifold closet doors. They slid open and I fell flat out on the floor, hitting the right side of my face, my arm, and my hip. The impact was hard, but I was not rendered unconscious. I laid there and cried out to God that I had to get up. No one was home but me and Him. I put my hand to my face to make sure it wasn't bleeding, then I proceeded to get up. I got up and said, "Thank You, God." Then I cried because my face hurt so bad. I called my mom, who wasn't home. I paged John, who was in a meeting. In the meantime, I went upstairs and looked in the mirror and saw a knot forming on the side of my face. I had hit my chin also. It pained me as well.

John called and I told him I had fallen, I didn't need to go to the hospital, but I was hurting. He said he would be home as soon as his meeting was over. I felt that I needed someone to pray for me, so I called my friend Tammye. She prayed and asked if I needed her to come over. I told her John was on his way and thanked her. I knew I was going to be all right because I had gotten up. Some people fall and don't get up. I praised and thanked God for being able to get up.

I wrote in my journal the next day, "Thank You, Lord for sustaining me. I will continue running the race, until I can run no more."

December 1993

The adversary had the audacity to try to attack me in church. I had just finished my Sunday school class and was walking down the aisle to retrieve my choir robe from the coat closet. Slowly I walked, programming my mind not to fall. As soon as the thought, *Don't fall,* flashed through my mind, down I fell. Saints rushed to help me up and asked if I was all right. I couldn't feel my legs at first, but when I could a chair was waiting for me. A sister in Christ, Inetha, who is a prayer warrior, came and rebuked any demonic spirit that was around me. I was thankful for her holy boldness. Tissues were handed me because the tears were flowing. "A determined spirit" was going to sing and not be discouraged by the fall. A soloist sang one of my encouragement songs, "When I See Jesus" by Douglas Miller, and I released praise and thanksgiving to God for being that "very present help" (see Ps. 46:1). The following day I was sore and bruised, but that was all. I had an attitude of thankfulness.

April 1994

I was at home, walking down the hall to go downstairs for a drink of water. My right foot did not move when I went to turn to go down the steps, so I fell into the linen closet doors and slid to the floor. Fortunately, I was able to maneuver my body so that I fell on my back and not my face. Stacey ran into the hall from her room crying, "Mom, get up!" I laid there straight out on my back collecting myself. She went to get her father who was downstairs in the office, and upstairs he ran. While I lay there I called on the name of Jesus to help me. When John came he asked, "Can you move?" I said, "Give me a minute so the messages can get to my brain to get up and to move my legs." I told him to stand in front of me and pull me up. He did, and I got up! Ashley slept through all of this in my room on the bed. She had wanted to sleep in my room with me, and I told her she could until her daddy came upstairs. I got in the bed and finally John came upstairs. He carried Ashley to her bed and I very slowly walked Stacey to her bed.

The next day my neck and elbow were both sore from hitting the floor. Otherwise I was fine. In my morning devotions I thanked God for sustaining me, and He told me that even in the midst of tribulation, nothing could separate me from the love of Christ (see Rom. 8:38-39). I was encouraged!

Burnt Hand

This accident happened September 29, 1994. Following my quiet time with the Father in prayer and devotions, I went upstairs to ask Stacey and Ashley what they wanted for breakfast. Both wanted a raisin muffin with an egg. Stacey wanted her egg scrambled, Ashley wanted hers fried. I mixed enough scrambled egg for John, Stacey, and myself and poured it into the pan. I reached to pick up the spatula which I had laid on the stove. I grasped the handle and burned my right hand, not realizing that the end of the spatula had slid into the gas flame and was on fire. I screamed and went to the sink and held my hand under the cold water. I kept screaming, and Stacey and Ashley started to scream. John came down from upstairs to see what was going on, saw me leaning over the sink, and thought I had cut myself. He tried to calm me down and find out what had happened. I kept crying because the pain was intense. I told him to fill a bowl with ice so I could immerse my hand in it. He got the ice and said, "Sharon, start praising the Lord. Say your healing Scriptures." I did as he told me, and the pain started to lessen. He had gotten my mind off of the circumstance and focused on Jesus. Ashley and Stacey had stopped screaming but were still crying.

John called a former neighbor friend of ours, Dr. Bland, advised him of the situation, and asked him to come over. He came right away and examined my hand. Boy, it hurt when he touched it! His initial concern was the possible severity of the burn. Finally, he said, "You're going to live, you only have a first degree burn." I thanked God! Dr. Bland extended himself further by going home to retrieve some pain medicine and an ointment for my hand. He applied the ointment then left and said, "Call me if you need me." I was thankful for his friendship and assistance.

That evening I had a healing class to go to. "A determined spirit" was going to have me present. I went, and the instructor and other class participants prayed over me after the session was over. When I left the class, I was opening and closing my hand. The next day my hand was slightly swollen and there was tenderness, but no pain. My hand had been healed. I was unable to write legibly with my right hand for a few weeks, there was weakness on the right side, and I was out of remission, but "a determined spirit" was not defeated. By November 1994, I was typing, writing, playing the piano, combing my hair, driving, and other things with the use of that hand. Praise the Lord, for "I can do all things through Christ who strengthens me" (Phil. 4:13).

Chapter 25

Routine Daily Difficulties

Yet in all these things we are more than conquerors through Him who loved us.

Romans 8:37

"Therefore we do not lose heart. Even though our outward man is perishing, yet the inward man is being renewed day by day" (2 Cor. 4:16). The impact of my MS related symptoms—including general weakness, walking difficulty, and optic neuritis—has increased my awareness that many of the things I must do on a daily basis have become increasingly more difficult. However, if I operated out of my own strength to meet my life's demands, I wouldn't be able to do it. I pray every day, "Lord, help me meet my life demands today," and He answers that prayer daily. If He didn't, I would have to sit still more and be active less.

Driving would become one of the biggest stresses in my routine, if I didn't pray and say my confession, "I am carefree, worry-free, burden-free, and anxiety-free in Jesus' name." With that daily confession and confidence in the command of Proverbs 3:5, "Trust in the Lord with all your heart, and lean not on your own understanding," I thank God for providing me with the strength and enablement to drive.

Although John normally takes Stacey and Ashley to school, I am responsible for picking them up every day, unless they go home with a friend or I have a doctor's appointment or treatment. In 1993, I began to have difficulty moving my right leg from the accelerator to the brake. We had a driving aid installed on the van, which controls the brake and accelerator with a lever arm on the steering wheel. Pushing the lever down controls the brake and pulling it at an angle controls the accelerator. What a blessing it has been! I pray asking for traveling mercy each time I leave to drive somewhere, and I pray a prayer of thanksgiving when I reach my destination. I know that angels are encamped all about me as I drive.

Because my reflexes are slowed, I must be especially alert when I drive to watch out for cars cutting in front of me, cars turning abruptly without a signal, and other things that most drivers have to be cognizant of. I used to drive very fast, but I don't any more. I obey speed limits, and at times, I may even drive slower. I try not to go too many places alone, because if I do, I have to know that there's someone to help me maneuver when I reach my point of destination. Sometimes Stacey says, "Mom, I wish I could drive so I could help you." *Sometimes* I wish she could be an experienced driver too.

Other difficult tasks are cooking and doing laundry, since for the most part, both require standing. I also have to lift and carry things, which isn't easy because of my need to hold onto a wall or some other stationary object in order to maintain my balance. John reminds me "in love" not to try to carry things, but sometimes I want something done immediately so I'll try to do it. Is that being hardheaded? Yes, but it keeps us communicating!

I love to cook. Our favorite dish is lasagna, which requires a lot of work. Ashley likes to assist me. When I make that dish, I tell my family to savor every taste and they do. While saying grace, they ask blessing both for the food and for the hands that prepared it! I do a lot of Crock-Pot meals as well as baking, broiling, and steaming. Frying food is really hard because if grease pops, it's hard to dodge; I usually have to stand over or sit near the food to watch it. I love baking cakes, but just lifting the mixing bowl can be a hard task when you're more weak than strong. Thank You, Lord, that Stacey and Ashley enjoy preparing what they can, especially desserts.

Some of the most simple tasks, like unscrewing the top from a jar, removing the lid of a medicine vial, threading a needle, and sewing, are not simple tasks for me anymore. I ask for help when I need it. Sometimes there are volunteers around to assist, sometimes not. When assistance isn't available, I'm just thankful to be able to do what I can. Accomplishment is a good feeling!

Among the things that perturb me most, is having to move things off of the floor or off the steps where I have to walk. It takes energy and balance to pick things up. Stooping is a no-no. I may be able to get down, but I have difficulty getting back up sometimes. To put away or retrieve pans from low cabinets, I have to get on my knees, but that's all right, because while I'm there I can pray. One day I asked John to make sure he always puts the television remote control where I can reach it, so I don't have to walk to get it on the other side of the room. He thanked me for the reminder. I point things out to Stacey and Ashley the same way. When you're not used to being conscious of even minute obstacles, you must train yourself and those around you.

When it comes to personal things—like showering, getting dressed, and doing my hair—these tasks can be a difficult, slow process. Honestly, it is very frustrating at times. That's why I like giving myself ample time to complete tasks, so I can take my time. Rush days are gone! "A determined spirit" has learned to take one day at a time as the inward man is renewed.

Chapter 26

My Grace Is Sufficient

Many are the afflictions of the righteous, but the Lord delivers him out of them all.

Psalm 34:19

God keeps speaking to me in my spirit from Second Corinthians 12:7-10:

And lest I should be exalted above measure by the abundance of the revelations, a thorn in the flesh was given to me, a messenger of Satan to buffet me, lest I be exalted above measure. Concerning this thing I pleaded with the Lord three times that it might depart from me. And He said to me, "My grace is sufficient for you, for My strength is made perfect in weakness." Therefore most gladly I will rather boast in my infirmities, that the power of Christ may rest upon me. Therefore I take pleasure in infirmities, in reproaches, in needs, in persecutions, in distresses, for Christ's sake. For when I am weak, then I am strong.

At least four times, beginning in February 1989, the Lord has said to me, "My grace is sufficient." With the same message being placed on my heart, I wanted to fully understand what the Lord was saying to me. So, under the guidance of the Holy Spirit, I began an intense study of Scripture, commentaries, and sermons to see how "My grace is sufficient" applied to me.

I began to understand that multiple sclerosis was my thorn in the flesh, and it was an opportunity for the power of Christ to be demonstrated in my life. I now know, after 13 years of living with MS, that I don't have to keep asking for this thorn to be removed. What an honor for God to tell me, "My grace is sufficient," because grace is something that we do not deserve, it is something we cannot earn. It is His unmerited favor!

God revealed so much to me through a sermon delivered by Dr. Charles Stanley, "Grace for Times of Trouble." I know God was speaking directly to me to give me clarity of mind! I now understand that as long as I have the thorn "multiple sclerosis," it is profitable for God's purpose. Hallelujah! I'm glad that "a determined spirit" has been chosen as a participant in God's demonstration of grace.

"My grace is sufficient" is an answer to prayer, just like "yes" or "no." When I was first diagnosed with multiple sclerosis, I did not want to suffer with MS. I wanted it to be removed. A thorn was not in *my* plans for myself. It was not the answer I sought. I wanted an immediate "yes" to healing: a physical manifestation that healing had occurred. But, the issue is what is the Father's will, not what is my will! Who was "a determined spirit" to be so bold to give God a timetable? Did I not have to learn humility and thankfulness? The Word clearly says, "In everything give thanks; for this is the will of God in Christ Jesus for you"

(1 Thess. 5:18). What better way to be taught these attitudes than with my thorn of multiple sclerosis? But, I have learned that "My grace is sufficient" doesn't rule out faith healing because God can choose to do whatever He wants to, when He wants to, and how He wants to. He's God! The Word tells me in Hebrews 11:6, "But without faith it is impossible to please Him, for he who comes to God must believe that He is, and that He is a rewarder of those who diligently seek Him." So my faith grows in the process of diligently seeking Him. God is my focus, not MS.

"My grace is sufficient" means that God is my everything. He will be my sufficiency that overflows and never ends. His love is inexhaustible for my pain and suffering. During the morning, noon, or night, Philippians 1:29 speaks to me, "For to you it has been granted on behalf of Christ, not only to believe in Him, but also to suffer for His sake." No, the thorn is not an easy thing to endure, but enduring the thorn in His righteousness brings glory to God. "A determined spirit" is learning how to respond to this circumstance, and God continues to make me into what He wants me to be. The answer "My grace is sufficient" places me in a position to mature. Oh what fruit that maturity can produce—fruit like love, joy, peace, patience, kindness, gentleness, and self-control.

"My grace is sufficient" allows me to rest in God. If the thorn is removed before the purpose is fulfilled, I won't learn how to rest in Him. The learning process, living daily with MS is the greatest demonstration of God's power. For it does more than change the circumstance around me; it is changing my heart so that I can rise above MS and praise the Lord anyhow. In every trial, I can get up, shake the dust off my feet, and give Him praise. Yes, I have begged, cried, and prayed for my circumstance to be different, but today I have a thankful heart, for I have been changed for the glory of God.

"A determined spirit" is willing to suffer for Christ's sake, for He lives inside of me. His indwelling is the source for everything I need. I'm able to express His power, love, and goodness. My prayer is as the songwriter William J. Kirkpatrick wrote in "Lead Me to Calvary": "May I be willing Lord to bear daily my cross for Thee; even thy cup of grief to share; Thou has borne all for me." The Spirit testifies that God is up to something *big* in my life as He allows MS to remain, while providing grace sufficient to bear the thorn. Hallelujah! He's awesome. As Paul said in Romans 8:18, "For I consider that the sufferings of this present time are not worthy to be compared with the glory which shall be revealed in us." Lord, Thou art the potter, I am the clay. Reveal Your glory in me!

Chapter 27

Endings

For of Him and through Him and to Him are all things, to whom be glory forever. Amen.

Romans 11:36

It's December 3, 1994, and this is the last chapter. I made it through it all. The story continues, but this book ends for now. I know that when God starts something, He finishes it, for He is the beginning and the end (see Rev. 21:6). I knew when I began *A Determined Spirit* that it was a task ordained long before I was born. For as recorded in Psalm 139:16, the Word says:

Your eyes saw my substance, being yet unformed. And in Your book, they all were written, The days fashioned for me, when as yet there were none of them.

This story was not one of my choosing, but it was a purpose God orchestrated and I pursued. I am thankful to Him for allowing me to suffer for Christ's sake. Had I not been allowed the multiple sclerosis thorn, how would I have known God as my healer, *Jehovah Rapfa*; the Lord as my shepherd, *Jehovah Raah*; and the Lord as my provider,

Jehovah Jireh? Would I have had such an intimate relationship with Him? I don't know!

I was led this year by the Spirit of God to study the Book of Philippians. What a blessing! What perfect timing, for there are so many things in Paul's letter about joy that I can relate to. I am encouraged by the entire letter, especially Philippians 1:6 where Paul writes, "Being confident of this very thing, that He who has begun a good work in you will complete it until the day of Jesus Christ."

Yes, I have days that I would rather be "...absent from the body and to be present with the Lord" (2 Cor. 5:8). However, my heart's desire is that "...Christ will be magnified in my body, whether by life or by death" (Phil. 1:20). As Paul says in Philippians 1:23, "For I am hard pressed between the two, having a desire to depart and be with Christ, which is far better." When I think about my struggles with MS being over, I just want to be with the Lord because sometimes the journey makes me weary. But, according to Philippians 1:22, "...if I live on in the flesh, this will mean fruit from my labor...." There are days when I have conversations with God and say to him, "Lord, I'm not Job, I'm not Paul, wouldn't you like to modify Your purpose for me?" Then I gather myself and realize that "a determined spirit" must focus on God's will, not my own, "for it is God who works in you both to will and to do for His good pleasure" (Phil. 2:13).

The trials and tribulations I have endured in my struggle with MS have led me to a more intimate relationship with my Lord and Savior Jesus Christ. I've come to understand that how we handle adversity has everything to do with our relationship with Him. He's not just our interceder, He's our friend. And one of the privileges, as well as responsibilities, of friendship is *knowing* your friend. I can honestly say that I have come to know Jesus as my friend and comforter, especially as I have more earnestly and diligently yielded myself to His lordship. Yet, as Paul says in Philippians 3:13-14:

> *Brethren, I do not count myself to have apprehended; but one thing I do, forgetting those things which are behind and reaching forward to those things which are ahead, I press toward the goal for the prize of the upward call of God in Christ Jesus.*

Studying the letter in Philippians taught me to have peace with others by rejoicing in the Lord always; to have peace with myself by being anxious for nothing; and, to have peace with my circumstances by remembering that "I can do all things through Christ who strengthens me" (Phil. 4:13). "A Determined Spirit" may sometimes feel battle worn, but never defeated. Through His grace and mercy, I press on, "For to me, to live is Christ, and to die is gain" (Phil. 1:21).

I leave you with the words of this song. "To Live Is Christ."[1]

> To live is Christ, and to die is gain
> To suffer with Him, I know that I shall reign
> In His arms, over there, in that land bright
>   and fair
> To live is Christ, oh Christ, and to die is gain.
> To suffer with Him, and to feel His pain
> To carry my cross is the reason why He came
> Just to save my soul, and to make me whole
> To live is Christ, oh Christ, and to die is gain

To gain my peace from the storms that tear
My heart into pieces, little bitty pieces
Where no love can dwell there.

To gain my robe, and to gain my crown
To live is Christ, oh Christ, and to die is gain

To gain my robe and to gain my crown
To suffer is Christ
To go through is Christ, oh to live is Christ
And to die is gain
To live is Christ and to suffer is Christ
To go through is Christ
Oh and to die is gain.

"Rejoice in the Lord always. Again I will say, rejoice!" (Phil. 4:4)

Notes

Introduction

1. Carol Antrom, "My Times," *Shekinah Glory*, LaShun Pace, (New York: Savoy Records, Inc., 1993).

Chapter 1/Beginnings

1. L.E. Campbell, "Something Within," The New National Baptist Hymnal, (Tennessee: National Baptist Publishing Board, 1977), 275.

Chapter 3/What's With the Numbness?

1. Dr. Charles M. Poser, *Multiple Sclerosis*, (New York: Raven Press, 1983), 17.

2. Ibid., 27.

Chapter 5/Diagnosis and Acceptance of Multiple Sclerosis

1. Ibid., 17.

2. Dr. Bryan Matthews, *Multiple Sclerosis, the Facts*, (Oxford: Oxford University Press, 1980), 16.

3. Quoted by Dr. Robert M. Herndon, reprinted from "Inside MS, Insight Into Eyesight," (New York: National

Multiple Sclerosis Society, 1985), *Facts & Issues*, Volume II, Number 3, 1. Used by permission.

4. Dr. Labe Scheinberg, *Multiple Sclerosis*, (New York: Raven Press, 1983), 116.

5. Ibid., 46.

6. Ibid., 3.

7. Ibid., 3.

8. Ibid., 33.

9. Louis J. Rosner, M.D. and Shelley Ross, *Multiple Sclerosis*, (New York: Prentice Hall Press, 1987), 143.

Chapter 6/What Is Multiple Sclerosis?

1. Ibid., 35.

2. Louis J. Rosner, M.D. and Shelley Ross, *Multiple Sclerosis*, (New York: Prentice Hall Press, 1987), 5.

3. Ibid., 5.

4. Ibid., 22.

5. "About Multiple Sclerosis," The National Multiple Sclerosis Society, 1978. Used by permission.

6. Dr. Labe Scheinberg, *Multiple Sclerosis* (New York: Raven Press, 1983), 36.

7. Ibid., 41-42.

Chapter 8/Pregnancy and Multiple Sclerosis

1. Ibid., 172.

2. Louis J. Rosner, M.D. and Shelley Ross, *Multiple Sclerosis*, (New York: Prentice Hall Press, 1987), 90.

Chapter 10/The Need For Other Professionals

1. Lynn Wasserman, comp. *Living With Multiple Sclerosis: Practical Guide,* (New York: The National Multiple Sclerosis Society, 1981), 9. Used with permission.

Chapter 15/Out of Remission Again

1. Dr. Labe Scheinberg, *Multiple Sclerosis,* (New York: Raven Press, 1983), 45.

Chapter 21/Sources of Strength

1. Walter A. Straughan, *By Jesus' 39 Stripes We Were Healed,* (Walter Straughan Ministries: Clinton, Maryland, 1991), 1-2.

2. D. E. King, *God's Word Shall Never Pass Away,* The New Progressive Baptist Hymnal spl. ed. of The New National Baptist Hymnal, (Tennessee: National Baptist Publishing Board, 1982), 424.

3. Darius Brooks, "For the Good of Them," *Available To You,* Kimberly McFarland with Rev. Milton Brunson and The Thompson Community Singers, (Illinois: A&M Records, 1988).

Chapter 27/Endings

1. Kirk Franklin, "To Live Is Christ," *In My Dreams,* Daryl Coley, (Tennessee: The Sparrow Corporation, 1994).

Ms. Moore, author of *A Determined Spirit*, welcomes comments and inquiries concerning the book. She may be contacted as follows:

Sharon Craft Moore
c/o Immanuel's Church
16819 New Hampshire Avenue
Silver Spring, MD 20905

HEALING THE WOUNDED SOUL
by Arline Westmeier.

It is generally understood that
Jesus died to forgive our sins and
to heal our sicknesses, but what
about our psychological wounds?
The author draws on her counseling experiences to show that Jesus
does heal His people from past
traumas, depression, inferiority
complexes, and other wounds of
the soul.
TPB-168p.
ISBN 1-56043-409-0
Retail $7.99